THE BURNING SUMMER

The stalls were already up this morning, their
awnings green and black and shabby in the bright
sunshine, the women who looked after them
already sitting in their old kitchen chairs next to
the cigar boxes they used to put their money in,
shouting across the street at each other, arguing
with the women who were shopping at the stalls.

Ruthie counted the stalls as they went by them.
Potatoes and carrots and onions and cabbages,
number one. The potatoes smelled of earth all
mixed up with a lovely hungry onion smell, and
the carrots were orange and green, the feathery
leaves at the top flopping over the edges of the
artificial grass sheet on the front of the stall.

The woman who kept the stall was digging the
dirty brass scoop from the scales into the pile of
potatoes so that the potatoes tumbled helter
skelter into it in a way that made Ruthie want to
bounce like they did.

THE BURNING SUMMER

Claire Rayner

ARROW BOOKS

For the children who came after

Arrow Books Limited
17-21 Conway Street, London W1P 6JD

An imprint of the Hutchinson Publishing Group

London Melbourne Sydney Auckland
Johannesburg and agencies throughout
the world

First published in Great Britain by Allison & Busby Limited
Arrow edition 1985

© Claire Rayner 1972

Printed and bound in Great Britain
by Anchor Brendon, Tiptree, Essex

ISBN 0 09 936690 8

CHAPTER ONE

RUTHIE had forgotten how noisy London was. She often forgot things like that, things she shouldn't really forget, and when grown-ups asked her about the things she had forgotten, and she said she didn't know, they got that stiff look on their faces.

Now she stood on the platform, with people rushing all round her, and the train grunting crossly behind her, and blinked at all the noise. Everything was such a dull colour, and she looked at all the brownness around her, and wondered about the colour. There were a lot of men, all wearing brown, a brown that looked like the water in the stream at the bottom of the auntie's garden, but she'd forgotten already. She had seen the garden only that morning, she knew that, but already she had forgotten what it was like.

"Right, ducks." The guard behind her put a hand on her shoulder and started to push her forwards, towards the end of the platform, and, obediently, Ruthie trotted along in front of him.

"We'll find your mum double quick now," the guard said, as Ruthie dodged past the legs of the men in brown who were walking about on the platform, carrying big sausage-shaped bags on their shoulders. "Soon find 'er, we will, and then you'll be all set, won't yer, ducks?"

"Yes," said Ruthie, a little breathlessly.

The man pushed her through the gate at the end of the platform, saying something to the man who was collecting tickets about "one of the vaccies", so that the man nodded and didn't seem to care that Ruthie hadn't got a ticket to give him.

Now they were in the big part of the station, and the noise was bigger, too. She could still hear the trains behind her, the rushing noise of steam, but now there were a lot more people, lots of men in brown, some in black, shouting at each other, laughing, banging things about.

She stopped walking, and tried to see her mother in all the crowd, and then suddenly she was very frightened, because she had forgotten again. What did Mummy look like? How would she know her? And would her mother remember what Ruthie looked like? She knew grown-ups didn't forget things as easily as she did, but perhaps her mother would have forgotten, all the same, and Ruthie would have to stay in this brown station for ever and ever.

She felt the crying that was always there inside her start to climb up her chest, pushing against her neck, and she tried to push it down with her tongue, holding it against her teeth to make a roof but the crying came up, very tight and pointed like a needle. Her mouth opened by itself, and the crying came out, loud and high, and her eyes got hot and big as the tears came out and ran down her face.

"It's all right, ducks," the man said, crouching down beside her, and wiping her face with his sleeve. "It's all right, ducks."

But Ruthie cried more and more, so that people stopped and looked at her. "Poor little mite—what's the matter? Lost her mum, has she?"

And then, suddenly, her mother was there, bending down next to the man, and putting her hands on her shoulders, and Ruthie knew she hadn't forgotten after all. It was Mummy, looking just the same, with her yellow hair, and her egg-shaped eyes with the line in between, and the red mouth with the double-pointed shape at the top of it.

"All right, Ruthie," she said, in her bright sharp voice, the one she used when other people were listening to her as well as Ruthie. "All right, Ruthie, nothing to cry about, dear—I'm here."

And now Ruthie's crying changed inside her, feeling different, warm and comfortable, and she felt her mouth go soft again, and began to enjoy the wetness on her cheeks.

The man was talking to her mother. "Right, lady. Here's her bag, now, and she's been fine—not a peep out of her, all the way down. It's a long run but not a peep out of her. Good little soul, she's been. Ta, lady."

And then he was gone, and Ruthie and her mother were together in the middle of the crowd of brown people.

"Come on, Ruthie."

Ruthie began to trot again, running along beside her mother, feeling the tears dry on her face, tasting the last of the salt of them on her upper lip, and holding on to her mother's hand very tightly.

They went to a big room, full of women, some of them in brown clothes like the men on the platform, a room full of smoke, and the high comfortable noise of women talking.

"Thank you—thanks a lot—hope he hasn't been any trouble," Ruthie's mother said to one of the women, stopping next to a big pram.

"No trouble at all, sweet little feller—he's a dear little chap."

Ruthie peered into the pram in some surprise. She'd forgotten about this, too. The baby. One of the aunties had told her there was a baby now, a brother, she'd said, a sweet little brother sent from God. Ruthie looked at the baby lying on his back in the pram, holding his hands in front of his very small face, staring at his fingers with blue eyes that had milky lines round the blue part, his mouth open and pink.

Her mother put Ruthie's suitcase on to the pram, and backed out of the waiting room with it, while the women peered into it, and smiled at the baby and made noises at him with their mouths.

"Hold on, Ruthie," her mother said, so Ruthie held on, and let the pram pull her along.

The street outside was very bright and hot, and smelled of dust and petrol, and Ruthie stared around her as they hurried along, looking up at the big red buses and the cars and the lorries.

"This is London," she said to herself, letting her mouth make the words, though she didn't let any sound come out. "This is London."

It was so funny to have forgotten, because it was just the same really. When she had lived in the auntie's house, in the houses of the other aunties, she had kept saying, "I want to go back to London", to everyone, even though she had quite forgotten what London was like. Now she was here, now she had been sent back, it was the same as it used to be, nearly the same. Some of the windows looked funny, shop windows with wooden fronts instead of glass ones, some of the glass ones with pretty patterns of brown paper criss-crossed all over them, and there were piles of brown sandbags along the pavements, stacked round big silvery bunkers. But the buses were the same, though they had brown paper criss-crossed on the windows too, and the cars and lorries were the same. So much brown.

While they waited to cross a road, she looked up at the sky, to see if that was the same, too, and then she stared, her head so far back she could feel her hair on her neck. Up in the sky, a blue sky with pretty clouds like pieces of cotton wool, there were fish, beautiful silver fish, with soft rainbow colours all round them, all round their fat tails. They were the most beautiful things she had ever seen, and Ruthie pulled on her mother's hand, and said, "Look—look, Mummy, look! Fish—lots of fish in the sky."

Her mother looked up briefly, and then began to cross the road, pushing the pram so quickly Ruthie had to run to keep up.

"Barrage balloons," she said. "That's what they are. Come on—it's a long way yet."

It was a funny name for such beautiful fish, Ruthie thought, and she ran along beside the pram, her head still back, staring at the fish moving lazily, turning a little, seeming to bounce a bit in the blue sky.

She began to get very tired after a while, as still they walked pushing the grey pavement away with their feet, and Ruthie's legs begn to feel very heavy and hot, and her feet hurt because they were so hot. She told her mother she was tired, but her mother just said, "Nearly there—not far now," and went on walking, bent a bit forwards over the pram, watching the people as they walked so that they wouldn't bump into them, her face very stiff and shut up. So Ruthie said no more about how tired she was.

And then, suddenly, they left the big main road they had been walking along, turning a corner next to a little sweet shop, and Ruthie stared at the street they were in.

It wasn't a very long street—she could see right to the end—and the funny thing about it was that at the end there wasn't just another road, but a shop, with a dark alleyway next to it, like a tunnel, and through the tunnel, Ruthie could just see a square of brightness with tiny people walking past.

There were houses on each side of the street, all joined together, with a door, and then two windows, and then another door, and then two windows, all the way on each side right to the end. Some of the doors were open, and there were wooden kitchen chairs outside them with women sitting in them, shouting across at other women sitting on chairs outside their doors.

Her mother stopped outside one of the doors, halfway down, and lifted Ruthie's case off the pram, to put it down next to the door. She took a key from her pocket, and opened the door, and Ruthie stared at the door, very surprised.

"Aren't we going home?" she asked. "I thought I was going home with you." She felt the crying begin to come up inside again.

"This is home," her mother said. "This is where we live now."

Ruthie tried to remember what home was supposed to be like, but she couldn't. She had forgotten again. She was sure it hadn't been here, in this street, but her mother said it was home now, So it was.

She followed her mother to the stairs inside the house,

staring at the narrow passage with its yellow and red lino on the floor, and a big brown curtain hanging across it beyond the stairs. At the top of the stairs, her mother stopped, and opened a door, and pushed Ruthie inside.

Ruthie stood and looked at the room, while her mother went downstairs again to fetch the baby. It was a small room, with a big window on one side, and a table in the middle, with two chairs next to it. There was a couch, and a sink, and a gas stove and a curtain hanging across the space under the sink, a pink curtain that Ruthie looked at happily. She liked pink. It was the nicest colour in this room, because mostly the room was brown and a sort of dirty yellow colour.

Her mother came back, holding the baby, and another woman came with her.

"So this is your Ruthie." The woman was very fat, and her head was very small, and it looked as though she hadn't got a neck at all, as though her head was stuck on her shoulders without a neck just like the people Ruthie made out of plasticine.

"So hello, Ruthie," the woman said, her voice wheezy, as though she wanted to cough. "So is it nice to be home again? You had to come home to your momma, hey? Couldn't stay in the country? So what was the matter? Didn't you like the country?"

Ruthie looked at her, and tried to remember the country. But she'd forgotten, of course, so she said, "I don't know," and the woman laughed, and pinched her cheek hard with a hand that smelled like cooking, all oniony.

Ruthie was very tired now. Too tired really to think much. It was so funny, suddenly to be so tired. She sat in a chair by the table, while her mother put a kettle on the gas stove, and the woman talked to her mother very wheezily, and the baby lay on the couch and made grizzly noises. Ruthie tried to listen to the woman, to understand what she was saying, but her voice just sounded thick, all soft and wheezy and thick, and Ruthie couldn't hear her words properly.

But then her mother started to talk.

"So what could I do? They told me, she kept running away—wouldn't stay anywhere. No sooner they settled her, but she was off again—found her in all sorts of places, they told me. So could I leave her there? I tell you, I got enough troubles without having her here in London— it's all I can do to look after me and the baby without her here as well, but what could I do? Leave her there? They said a hostel, but they tried one, and she carried on there —ran off again. So what could I do?"

The woman looked at Ruthie then, sitting at the table, and said in her thick wheezy voice, "So why you keep running off, Ruthie? Why don't you stay in the country like a good girl? Your mother's got enough troubles, believe me. She shouldn't have to worry about such a big girl like you—seven you are, Ruthie, a big girl. Why you keep running off like that?"

Ruthie blinked at her, and said again, "I don't know,"

and she really didn't. She couldn't remember anything about the country, anything at all. So all she could say was, "I don't know."

Her mother gave her a piece of bread and butter, and some cheese and a big cup of tea, and while she was eating, while the woman and her mother went on talking, she tried very hard to remember about the country, about running away, but it was no good.

Her mother put her to bed, then, in another room, a room with a bed and a cot in it, and she fell asleep too quickly to think about anything at all any more.

CHAPTER TWO

RUTHIE was sitting on the edge of the pavement, her dress spread carefully all round her, enjoying the warmth that came up from the hot kerbstone through her thin knickers. There were two reasons for sitting there. First because the warmth was so nice, travelling up through her skin right through her bottom to meet the heat that was coming down through her shoulders from the sun above; and secondly, there was always the hope that the warmth would dry her knickers which were a bit wet already. She hadn't been up for long, and it would be a while yet before her mother would call her from the window to come and go to the lavatory. By that time, perhaps her knickers would be dry, and her mother wouldn't know she had wet them so early in the day.

So she sat, blinking a little in the bright sunshine, stroking the brown rexine case of her gas mask, letting her thumbnail run along the grooves, enjoying the possession of the lovely thing. Ruthie loved her gas mask. It was her very own, given to her by the Government, and they had told her it was her special one, that she must never leave it lying around, that no one must ever take it away from her. It was hers as nothing else had ever been. Her clothes belonged to her mother. Whenever she got new dresses, her mother reminded her that they cost a lot of money, that they weren't bought to be spoiled, that Ruthie must take care of them because her mother had to struggle so hard to buy them for her. So Ruthie could never really enjoy ownership of the things she wore as she could enjoy the ownership of her gas mask the Government had given her.

Ruthie was very attached to the Government. She had a hazy vision of him: an old man in a long white night-dress, with a big white beard like Mr Lipshitz's. When she thought of him, she saw a big map of England, with the Government sitting on a big chair in the bottom left-hand corner, down in Cornwall. The children from next door were down there with him. They had been sent down there to be with him away from London when the war started, like Ruthie. Only they were still there. Her mother told her that quite often.

Across the road, Mrs Levy came out with a broom to sweep the pavement. Ruthie's mother was always very rude about Mrs Levy, though never to her face, of course. When she met her, she would nod and smile, and say nice things like it was hot again, wasn't it? But when she was sitting upstairs in her window, and saw Mrs Levy come out with her broom, she would snort, and say, "Look at her! Silly old cow! Sweeping the road, yet! Got eyes in her toochus, that one. What she can't see from her window, she's got to come out and watch with her broom."

Ruthie would stare down at Mrs Levy, and try to imagine what it was like to have eyes in your toochus. Once she had peered over her own shoulder while her mother was washing her, and said, "Have I got eyes in my bottom, like Mrs Levy?" and her mother had slapped her lightly and laughed. So Ruthie still didn't know. She used to wonder if Mrs Levy kept the eyes in her bottom closed, or open, and whether she cut holes in her knickers so that she could see through with the extra eyes, but she knew better than to ask Mrs Levy. Mrs Levy had no teeth, and Ruthie didn't like talking to her, because her mouth looked so empty and black when she opened it.

Ruthie looked away from Mrs Levy, in case she should call across to her, and looked down the street towards Black Sophie's shop at the end. There wasn't much to see yet. There were two women standing talking outside the shop, with big plaited straw shopping bags hanging flat and empty from their hands, their heads close together as they talked. One of them was Mrs Coram, who lived three doors away from Ruthie, and Ruthie stared at her, at the tight waves of her wig, and the deep lines on her thin face. She liked Mrs Coram because of her wigs. She had two, one she wore every day of the week, and one she wore on Saturdays. Her mother had told her that Mrs Coram was very froom, and that meant she went to the synagogue every Saturday and wore a special wig.

"Religious people wear wigs," Ruthie's mother said. "They cut all their hair off when they get married and make wigs out of it, and then they wear them on top of their hair ever afterwards."

Ruthie thought it must be nice to get married, and cut your hair off and wear a wig. It would be much nicer than having your own hair brushed with a wire brush, that had long thin nails stuck in rubber, and pulled the knots till your eyes watered. Not that she was very hopeful of ever getting married like Mrs Coram was. Her mother was married, and she hadn't cut her hair off.

Ruthie had asked why not, once, when her mother was doing her hair with stuff in a saucer and an old toothbrush, but her mother had told her to stop nagging, and screwed her face up against the smell of the ammonia. So Ruthie wasn't quite sure what would happen when she got married herself.

From the door next to Black Sophie's shop, Lilian came out. Lilian was a big girl—nearly nine—and Ruthie liked her. She had yellow hair, just like Ruthie's mother's hair the day after she had used the toothbrush and the ammonia, and she had it in smooth straight pieces on each side of her face. Ruthie admired this hair style very much, and would have liked to have yellow straight hair instead of her own black curls that got into knots.

Lilian came over the street carefully not walking on

any cracks. She stopped next to Ruthie, and stood on one foot.

"You goin' to school?"

"Don't know," Ruthie said. "Was there a raid last night?"

"Don't know. They didn't get me up. My mum's still in bed, though. Maybe there was."

"My mummy's up. But she gets up even if there was a raid. Because of Leon."

Lilian nodded. "You got to get up when you got a baby," she said knowingly. "They cry."

Ruthie knew that very well. Leon cried in the mornings, because he was hungry. She would lie in bed in the mornings, looking across at him in his cot, his fat face creased while he bawled, wishing he didn't cry when he was hungry. When he cried like that, her mother woke up and made her get up, and if she hadn't woken before Leon started crying, it meant she hadn't time to fix things before her mother found out about her bed.

This was Ruthie's biggest problem. Every night when she went to bed, she would lie very straight, screwing her toes up hard till they hurt, biting her bottom lip till that hurt too, praying to God. If she could hurt her toes and her lip very much while she prayed, perhaps God would listen to her, and not let her wet her bed. But it never worked.

"Don't let me wet my bed, please, God," she would say inside her head. "Don't let me wet my bed." But she couldn't hurt her toes and her lip enough, because she always wet her bed.

When she first woke up, when the light first made the place inside her eyes red and sparkling, she would lie very still, not moving at all, because until she moved, she wouldn't know, wouldn't be sure. While she was quite still, she could tell herself God had listened, that she was dry today. But then she would move a little bit, tightening her bottom, and then she would know, feeling the warm dampness, smelling the thick familiar smell.

If she had woken before Leon and her mother she could get up, and rearrange her bed, putting the wet part of the sheets to the bottom, so that if her mother was busy and only pulled the bed up instead of stripping it properly, she wouldn't find the wetness. She could fold up her wet nightgown, and put it at the bottom of the clothes in the cupboard, and put on a dry one, and the wet one at the bottom would stay there till it worked its way to the top, and by then maybe it would be dry again.

It was silly, really. None of the tricks ever worked; her mother always found out in the end, and Ruthie would be walloped for being sly as well as being a pisher, which was what her mother called her with her voice full of coldness. But still Ruthie tried.

Once she had crept out of bed after she had been put there, and put a thick layer of newspaper under her, because she thought that then the wetness wouldn't go through to the sheets, and she could throw the paper away in the dustbin in the morning. But the wetness had gone through, and worse still, the blackness from the printing on the paper had gone through, too, and made the sheet all black, and her mother had given her a hiding.

It was a dreadful business, really. She would have to stand in the street beside her mother, feeling her face go hard and stiff while she listened to her mother telling the neighbours about her wetness, listened to them tutting as they looked at her with disapproval, telling her she was a naughty girl to be so dirty when her mother had such troubles already. She would see the sheets from her bed hanging out of the upstairs window of the house as she came along the street, with the tell-tale round stain in the middle, drying in the sun, so all the world would know that Ruthie was a pisher, a dirty girl who made trouble for her poor mother.

"So are you going to school?" Lilian said again. "My mum's asleep, so I can if I like."

"I'll ask," Ruthie said, and stood up carefully. Her knickers were dry, so she ran into the house happily, letting her gas mask in its brown rexine case bang comfortingly against her bottom.

She ran up the stairs into the kitchen where her mother was sitting at the table with Leon on her lap, playing with him.

Leon was laughing, his round face screwed up fatly, his two white teeth shining in his red mouth, and giggling delightedly as his mother rubbed her nose against his.

"Kutchie, kutchie, kutchie," Ruthie's mother said,

screwing her eyes up like Leon's. "Kutchie, kutchie, kutchie!"

"Mummy," Ruthie said, "am I going to school? Lilian wants to know am I going to school."

Ruthie's mother put Leon on the floor so that he could crawl about, and stretched.

"I dunno." She yawned so that the two gaps in her teeth on each side of the front ones showed, and Ruthie looked away. "You want to go?"

"If Lilian goes. Her mum's still asleep, so she doesn't know if there was a raid last night. Was there a raid last night, Mummy?"

"Not much." Ruthie's mother rubbed her face and looked vaguely worried. "Not much. Not to get up for. You want to go?"

"Yes. If there wasn't a raid, I can, can't I?"

"Oh, all right—only listen to me. If there should be a siren, you know what to do?"

"Stay with Miss Fletcher, don't run, walk, do what Miss Fletcher says, stay in the middle of the shelter, don't sit near the wall, don't come out till last."

"And come straight home at dinner time. None of your dawdling. And go to the lav now," she called after Ruthie who was already halfway down the stairs.

So Ruthie came back and went into the lavatory, and stood for a minute before she pulled the chain noisily and ran down the stairs to Lilian. She didn't want to go to the lav now, but it wouldn't do to say so.

"All right," she said to Lilian, and the two of them walked up the street to the alleyway at the end.

The alleyway was the narrow covered passage that ran alongside Mrs Cohen's grocery shop to Festival Street beyond, and although it was supposed to be a private alley for the shop people and the family who lived in the flat over the top, no one ever went round the other way, to the bottom of the street, round the corner, along Commercial Road to the beginning of Festival Street.

Mrs Cohen was in front of her shop as they went by, and grinned at them.

"So where you goin'?"

"School," Lilian said. "We're going to school. There wasn't a big raid last night, so we can go to school this morning."

"Gott se dank," Mrs Cohen said, and gave them some broken biscuits from the box on the shelf in the front of the shop window.

They went along Festival Street eating the biscuits, Lilian walking a bit in front of Ruthie, and getting most of the biscuits because Lilian was nearly nine and Ruthie was only seven so she had to do what Lilian said. And Lilian had said a long time ago that she was always to walk in front and get most of everything.

Ruthie was very lucky to be friends with Lilian, and she knew it. There were only a few children left now in the street. Most of them had gone away. There were three girls older than Lilian, but they were friends with each other; they didn't want to be friends with Lilian because her mother wasn't Jewish like their mothers. But Ruthie's mother didn't seem to mind who Ruthie was friends with as long as she kept out of the way and out of trouble, so when Lilian started to be friends with Ruthie, Ruthie was very happy. There was no one in the street her own age—only another baby the same age as Leon, and Leon himself, and you couldn't be friends with babies.

So she walked along Festival Street behind Lilian, eating the soft broken biscuits and she was happy. She liked Festival Street. It wasn't as big or as noisy as Commercial Road, but it was much bigger than Aspen Street where they lived. Aspen Street had two shops— Mrs Cohen's and Black Sophie's—and houses. But Festival Street had lots of different shops, and a school, and stalls as well.

The stalls were already up this morning, their awnings green and black and shabby in the bright sunshine, the women who looked after them already sitting in their old kitchen chairs next to the cigar boxes they used to put their money in, shouting across the street at each other, arguing with the women who were shopping at the stalls.

Ruthie counted the stalls as they went by them. Potatoes and carrots and onions and cabbages, number one. The potatoes smelled of earth all mixed up with a lovely hungry onion smell, and the carrots were orange and green, the feathery leaves at the top flopping over the edges of the artificial grass sheet on the front of the stall.

The woman who kept the stall was digging the dirty brass scoop from the scales into the pile of potatoes so that the potatoes tumbled helter skelter into it in a way that made Ruthie want to bounce like they did.

She didn't like the next stall so much. It was full of chickens, dead ones, hanging up by their feet with flattened bloody eyes glinting wickedly at her as she went past, the feathers round their long necks hanging loosely into a big ruff round the pimply skin on their plucked breasts. The woman who kept this stall had a big blue apron on, and it was smeared all black and purple with the blood she wiped on it from the big knife she used to cut the chickens open. She stood hugely in front of the scored chopping board at the front of the stall, the big knife glinting gaily in the sun as she slit the birds open, pulling the guts out of each one with a twist of her big red hand, tossing the waste into a smelly barrel at her side, dropping the smooth livers and crops into the chipped enamel dish in front of her. Sometimes Ruthie stayed to watch her, horribly fascinated by the yellow globules that were eggs without shells, the blue and green smoothness of the strings of entrails, the way the skin of the throats peeled off to show the curving reddish brown neck underneath. When her mother cooked a chicken she would put this piece into the soup, and called it the gorrigle, and Ruthie liked it, picking it up in her fingers to pull at the strips of chicken meat from

25

the chain of little bones, with her teeth. But she was always sickened a bit when she watched the gorrigle being stripped of its skin covering at the chicken woman's stall.

The next stall was apples and pears and plums and bananas, not many bananas because there was a war on and you couldn't get them like you used to do. They would be sold very quickly, the shoppers buying more apples and pears than they really wanted so that the woman who kept the stall would let them buy the yellowish green bananas. Ruthie liked this stall very much, because the woman who kept it was often sleeping in her chair as she went by, and if she was quick, she could take an apple from the front without being caught.

The next two stalls were vegetables again, one of them kept by an old man who always wore a skull-cap, and who wore a heavy black suit all the time, even today when it was so hot the road seemed to wobble when you looked at it. It seemed to Ruthie that all the men in the world were old men with skull-caps and beards like this stall-holder and Mr Lipshitz at the synagogue. Sometimes there were men in brown uniforms, but they weren't men, they were soldiers, nebbish. The women in Aspen Street always said Nebbish after they said soldier, and Ruthie thought that Nebbish was part of the word soldier, though she knew it was also a word you used about anything sad, like a baby who banged his head and cried, nebbish.

Lilian was waiting to cross the road, looking back

impatiently at Ruthie who was walking backwards past the last fruit stall, enjoying the green and red of the apples that were piled there.

"Come *on*," she said. "Come *on*, Ruthie."

So Ruthie came on, running with high steps so that her gas mask banged on her bottom, happy because she was going to school and her knickers were dry, and Mummy hadn't done more than smack her once when her bed was wet that morning.

CHAPTER THREE

MISS FLETCHER and Mrs Ward were sitting at a big desk at the end of the assembly hall, the pile of registers in front of them. Lilian moved away from Ruthie as soon as they both came into the playground, making it quite clear to Ruthie that now they had arrived they were separate people again, not friends. You couldn't be nine and friends with someone from the infants who was only seven, not when you were inside the school. So Ruthie went into the assembly hall where Miss Fletcher and Mrs Ward were sitting with the registers.

There were hardly any children at the school because of the war, only enough for one class, a class that stayed in the assembly hall all the time, and the classrooms were empty, with all the chairs put on the desks, and only benches to sit on in the assembly hall.

Ruthie walked to Mrs Ward and Miss Fletcher round the edge of the assembly hall. This was because you could still make footprints round the edges. The dust in the middle was all scratched up where people had walked to the benches, but round the edges it was thick enough to make footprints. Miss Fletcher sighed when she looked at the dust in the hall, and shook her head because there was no one around who would work at the school to clean it, and she had too much to cope with to start sweeping the place herself, didn't she?

Miss Fletcher smiled at Ruthie and made a mark on the register.

"Hello, Ruth," she said in her thin voice that was all flat in the middle when she talked, not round and fat like the people in Aspen Street talked. "How is our only infant?"

"Hello, Miss," Ruthie said.

"Did you get up last night, Ruth, for the raid?" Miss Fletcher asked.

"No, Miss. Mummy said it wasn't much of a one. Not to get up for." Privately, Ruthie thought it couldn't have been a raid at all, really. You got up for real ones, and she hadn't got up, so there hadn't been one. But Miss Fletcher thought there had, so she didn't like to say there hadn't.

"Get some beads, Ruth," Miss Fletcher said. "Get some beads for now, and when everyone is here, we'll do something else."

So Ruthie went to the cupboard in the corner and got some beads and sat on a bench to string them up into a big wooden necklace while Miss Fletcher and Mrs Ward marked the registers and collected all the children together.

They did singing. Mrs Ward sat at the piano, with her bottom hanging over the edge of the seat, and played loudly, lifting her hands very high in the air all the time. Ruthie liked this very much, and when there was piano playing on the wireless at home, she would play on the edge of the table lifting her hands high like Mrs Ward did.

They sang some songs that Ruthie knew, and a lot she didn't, but she moved her mouth as though she were singing, sticking her tongue in and out to show she was singing the right words though she knew herself she was only pretending, and that it was scribble singing. One of the songs was called "Jerusalem", and she didn't look at Miss Fletcher waving her head and hands at the front while that one was being sung, because Miss Fletcher's eyes always went red and hot looking while it was on, and she wiped them afterwards. Ruthie found herself go hot and frightened inside when she saw grown-ups do that. Grown-ups who cried were awful.

There was milk and a biscuit after the singing. Mrs Ward brought the biscuits, and they were very dry, not soft and sweet like Mrs Cohen's broken ones, but Ruthie always ate Mrs Ward's out of politeness.

It was while she was finishing her milk, looking deep into the cup to see her face reflected in the shiny whiteness inside, that the sound came. It started soft, a long way away, and then it came closer, going up and down, high and thin, like Leon when he cried at bedtime. He cried differently when he was hungry, but at bedtime, just before he fell asleep, he cried high and thin like the siren.

Mrs Ward dropped the biscuits in their tin and started to cluck at the children, while Miss Fletcher picked up the registers and put them under her arm. Until now the children had been good, doing what Mrs Ward and Miss Fletcher said, but now they knew it was all right to be naughty, and began to jump about, and run in and out of the benches, squealing at each other. Ruthie did too, because the others did, getting excited with them.

Mrs Ward and Miss Fletcher shooed them along, collecting them into a long line, and hurried them out of the assembly hall, along the corridor to the playground.

The playground was very hot, the grit sparkling with tiny flashes of red and blue the way it did on sunny days, and Ruthie wriggled her toes in her sandals, enjoying the hot feeling and the smell of tar, pushing her feet into the hot tarmac so that she made footprints in its soft hotness, walking very quickly behind the big girl in front who was running. She wasn't to run when there was a siren, like you didn't run across roads. You had to walk, and it was very good to see how fast you could walk without running.

Already, there were some women at the gate, and as the children crossed the playground towards the big redbrick shelters on the boys' side, one or two of them came hurrying into the playground to pull their children out, chivvying them along before them.

Mrs Ward, behind Ruthie, tutted. "Stupid creatures—

anything could happen before they get them back to their own shelters."

Ruthie could quite understand why some of the mothers came to take their children to their own shelters. The school shelter wasn't nearly so nice as some of the ones in Aspen Street. The school shelter had rows of benches, and some buckets with lids on them in the corners, and piles of sandbags inside as well as outside. The lights were smelly, oil ones, and there weren't very many of them, so that the corners of the big shelter were dark. Ruthie had been surprised when her mother told her always to stay in the middle of the shelter because it was safer there. She was surprised because she hadn't thought her mother knew about the darkness in the corners, and how frightening it was there.

Mrs Ward and Miss Fletcher sat them all down in rows on the benches, and Miss Fletcher started to read a story, one about Joseph and the coat of many colours, while Mrs Ward stayed near the door, her head on one side as it was when she listened to things. Ruthie didn't listen to the story. She had suddenly discovered her knickers were wet again, and she felt miserable in the way she always did as she felt the dampness strike her skin when she sat on the cool wooden bench. While Miss Fletcher's voice went on about Joseph, Ruthie began to make up a story for her mother.

The other children were all using the buckets, that was why she couldn't get to one in time. When the siren went, she was just going to the lavatory, but it was too late, Miss Fletcher wouldn't let her go. Mrs Ward made her drink all her milk when she wasn't thirsty and that had made her get wet, she couldn't help it because of drinking all the milk when she wasn't thirsty. She had to think of the story she would tell carefully, because the shelter was a cool place, and her knickers wouldn't get dry sitting there, not like sitting on the kerb in the hot sun. And after a siren, her mother was always more cross than usual, and Ruthie would need a good story to get over that.

It wasn't a very long siren. Miss Fletcher hadn't finished the story of Joseph when the all-clear came.

"They must be going further over," Mrs Ward said, waiting till the all-clear from the near place took up the sound, not trusting the one that came softly from further away. "Come along, children. All clear—come along."

They stayed in the playground after that, running about in the hot sun, throwing bean bags to each other, standing in line to do exercises, turning their bodies from one side to the other while Mrs Ward called, "One and two and one and two. . . ."

When it was time to go home for dinner, Miss Fletcher gave them all books to take with them.

"Try and read these books yourselves at home," she said, as she put a book carefully into each child's hand. "And tomorrow we may be able to have a real lesson about them. Ruth—er—well, dear, you can take one, too. But don't worry if you can't read it properly. I'll try to help you tomorrow. . . ."

When they were outside the school gate, back in Festival Street, Lilian came to walk next to Ruthie.

"What you got a book for? You can't read this one properly. It's a hard book—for juniors, and you're an infant."

"I can read," Ruthie said defensively. "I'm seven. I can read."

"Not hard books like this," Lilian said. "You shouldn't be here, anyway. You should be evacuated with the other infants."

"So should you. All children should be. Juniors as well."

"My mum can't do without me," Lilian said smugly. "I'm all she's got. She couldn't bear to let me go. That's why I'm not evacuated. Not like you, runaway. Piddle-the-bed, runaway, piddle-the-bed!"

"I'm not!" Ruthie shouted "I'm not—I'm not! You're a shickser—you're a shickser!"

Lilian pinched her hard, and ran in front of her to dance up and down, waving her hands in Ruthie's face.

"I'm better than a piddle-the-bed Jew-girl. Piddle-the-bed Jew-girl! It was you Jews started the war—piddle-the-bed! Piddle-the-bed . . ."

And she spat hard in Ruthie's face, and ran across the road leaving Ruthie to go home by herself. Ruthie was very upset by this. It was dreadful to spit, the worst thing you could do. When she had done it once, trying to make the spit go through the bars of a drain while she sat on the kerb, her mother had come out to her, and

34

smacked her hard, shouting at her. It was filthy to spit
—vulgar.

So Ruthie went home on her own, sad about Lilian.
To spit and not to be Jewish—it was an awful thing.
Worse than wetting your bed, really, though that was
bad enough.

There was a bicycle leaning against the wall next to
the front door when she got to the house, and Ruthie
went cold inside. It was the woman from the Council
again, come to see her mother. When she came, her
mother got angry, and after the woman had gone, she
was worse than usual to be with, even worse than after
a siren.

So Ruthie went to the lavatory before she went into
the front room upstairs, opening the door wide when
she pulled the chain so that her mother would hear and
know she'd been a good girl.

The woman was sitting in a chair by the table, papers
in front of her, and her mother was standing against the
window, holding Leon, who squirmed and dug his feet
into her middle so that she had to keep moving him
from arm to arm.

Ruthie slipped into the room and went to stand next
to her mother, close, so that she wouldn't be seen very
easily.

"Really, Mrs Lee, it would be better," the woman said,
smiling at Ruthie very widely. "Hello, dear. How are
you?"

Ruthie said nothing, only staring at the woman.

"She's fine," Ruthie's mother said loudly. "Best off where she is, right here with me. She's a problem child, so she's best with me."

"I quite see that, Mrs Lee." The woman's voice was bright and she spoke slowly and evenly, like Mrs Ward did when she talked to Rachel Kaye who was a bit slow. "I do understand. But with a baby like yours you could go together, you see. I can't promise you, of course, but we might be able to find you a proper home, not a hostel, though perhaps it would have to be a hostel for a little while . . ."

"I'm not going," Ruthie's mother said. "I've got to stay here. My husband . . ."

"But, Mrs Lee, I've told you—we'd be able to let him know where you are. We'd see he found you . . ."

"Sure—just like that." Ruthie's mother sounded thick suddenly. "You'll find him. Like I haven't been trying for weeks? How can you find him if I can't? They've been looking for him long enough . . ."

The woman looked warningly at Ruthie, and interrupted.

"Have you been to school, dear? What lessons did you have this morning?"

"There was a siren," Ruthie said.

"Oh—yes, of course. A siren. Well, next time you go to school, perhaps you can have proper lessons, mm? You see, Mrs Lee? There's her education to think about, too, isn't there? As well as your safety . . ."

"Ruthie, go to Mrs Cohen's. Get me some lockshen,

36

and a quarter of cream cheese—go on." Ruthie's mother shoved her forwards, reaching round Leon to her apron for her purse, then dropping her hand before it got there. "Tell her to book it."

So Ruthie went running along Aspen Street quickly. She liked going to Mrs Cohen's. It smelled nice in her shop, and the old woman would give her little pieces of herring, or rings of white pickled onion that made her mouth water at the smell, even before she put it in her mouth, sometimes giving her whole green pickled cucumbers she could suck the seeds out of.

It was all very funny, this business with the woman from the Council. Like the soldiers nebbish who came sometimes. Whatever it all was, Ruthie knew it was about her father, who was a soldier nebbish as well. When people talked to her mother about her father, they looked sideways at Ruthie, and sent her away, not just telling her to go and play like they did when it wasn't anything special, but making errands for her to do. That was how she knew it was something she wasn't to know about.

Mrs Levy asked her once if she missed her daddy, and Ruthie had just looked at her and said, "Yes," because that was the right thing to say. But she didn't really.

They had been in Ireland when the war broke out, she and Mummy and Daddy. She'd been playing in the street, and he had come to get her.

"We're going on a ship, lovey," he'd said, and Ruthie had been glad. They'd come to Ireland on a ship, and

Daddy had laughed when they went on it, smiling at Ruthie's mother, saying it'd be all right this time, he'd be careful in future, no more running off. And Ruthie's mother had raised one eyebrow, and said she'd believe that when it happened.

But the war had come, so they went on a ship again, and it had been full of people being very sick. Ruthie had looked at all the people being sick, and her mother had taken her arm and held it very tight and stared at her with one eyebrow up the way she did when she was angry, and talked with only her mouth, keeping her teeth shut. "Don't you dare be sick," she'd said very quietly. "Just you dare . . ." and Ruthie hadn't.

Then they had got on a train, and Ruthie had fallen asleep. She had woken up, feeling sore with her legs cold and prickly because she had been lying on them pulled under her, and she had seen her mother standing on her toes kissing her father through the little window that was open on the top, and her hair had looked funny with a blue light on it from the only bulb in the middle of the railway carriage.

"Where's Daddy going?" Ruthie had asked, when she realised that her father was outside the train and they were staying inside it.

"To the army," Ruthie's mother said and Ruthie knew better than to ask any more questions.

Ruthie's mother had talked about him at first before Ruthie had been sent away to the country, reading bits out of letters from him, bits like "Tell Ruthie to be a good girl and not to wet her bed", or "Tell Ruthie to be a help to you and look after you for me".

But since Ruthie had been sent back from the country she hadn't talked about him, at all, didn't read bits out of letters because there weren't any letters.

Mrs Cohen's shop had a lot of people in it when Ruthie went in. She stood by the counter for a long time, trying to make Mrs Cohen see her, but she was talking to the other women.

"Terrible, it was," one of the women said. "I tell you, you shouldn't know of such things. In the next house to my Sadie, seven of them went—seven in one go. The house wall, right on the shelter it went, and seven of them there was in there. My Sadie, she said when she come out it was like she was in a strange country—none of the street was there, all a pile of stones. And when she goes to look for her own house, the things she sees —you shouldn't know of such things . . ."

"Must you talk of it then? Bad enough it happens, without you talk of it . . ." This from Mrs Salmon who had one of the big girls who lived in the street, one of the big four ones who wouldn't play with Lilian or Ruthie.

"So? You shut your eyes it goes away?"

"I tell you, if a bomb got your name on it, it got it. What can you do? You wait and see! So if it happens, it happens. You don't talk of it. You just wait and you live ordinary and you don't talk of it. You stay together, and if it happens, you go together. What else?"

"My Sadie, she's gone. Gone out to the country. And,

I tell you, if she gets a place, I go, too. I don't wait for no bomb with my name on it. Soon as she gets a place, I go to her and the children, God bless them."

Mrs Cohen laughed, fat and happy. "I can see you! I can see you living in the country. I go mad out of London, and so would you. So we stay—like me, you stay. I tell you, you go Monday to your Sadie in the country, so Friday I cut a herring ready for you like usual, you'll come back. Don't give me none of your stories."

"It's true, as I stand here, it's true, Mrs Cohen. You don't eat no herrings when a bomb got your name on it. I go to the country and do without herrings—but I eat! Better eat no herrings than eat nothing because you ain't alive to do it . . ."

Mrs Salmon caught sight of Ruthie standing against the high counter, and said sharply, "Shvag—der kinder," and Ruthie put on the blank face she always did when people said that. It meant that she shouldn't have heard what was already said and shouldn't hear what was going to be said, so it was best to look as though you hadn't been listening anyway.

"Please can I have some lockshen and a quarter of cream cheese?" she said.

"Sure, Ruthie, sure. You got the money?"

"Mummy said book it."

Mrs Cohen turned her mouth downwards and started to nod her head up and down resignedly as she weighed the cream cheese.

"Always I should book it—book it! I got books just for Mrs Lee to fill up and never clear?"

"So what can you do?" Mrs Salmon said comfortably. "You let children go hungry because . . ." she looked sharply at Ruthie—"you know why because."

Mrs Cohen licked a pencil and wrote in the blue book that hung from a piece of string next to the cash register.

"Sure, I know. Do you see me saying no? So I book it! Voos machst du? There's a war on! While I got, I give. Your mummy clear the book when she can, eh, Ruthie?"

And Ruthie took the cream cheese and the blue bag full of yellow twists of egg vermicelli and nodded, not quite sure what else to do but nod.

"Yes, Mrs Cohen, thank you, Mrs Cohen," she said, and ran home, to take the things up to her mother.

The bicycle had gone when she got there, and she went upstairs slowly, not sure whether her mother would be as usual, or angrier than ever because of the woman from the Council and having to book things at Mrs Cohen's.

CHAPTER FOUR

You could never tell how people would be. Instead of being cross, and nagging Ruthie after the woman from the Council had been, as she usually did, Ruthie's mother was happy and warm.

They had a lovely dinner, lockshen and milk, with cheese sprinkled on the top and apples afterwards, and they played the Ruthie-is-Mummy-and-Mummy-is-Ruthie game. Ruthie liked this. She sat in Mummy's place at the table, and told her mother what to do, to eat her dinner up like a good girl, and Ruthie's mother sat small in Ruthie's usual chair and said, "Yes, Mummy. Can I have a sweet if I eat all my dinner up, Mummy?" and Ruthie looked stern and said, "We'll see. You eat your dinner up first and don't make a mess on your dress and then we'll see." It was a very good game.

After dinner, they tidied up together, putting the dishes in the cupboard under the sink, straightening the cover on the couch so that the broken part on the arms didn't show, and sweeping the floor. Ruthie was allowed to shake the mat out of the window, and when she accidentally dropped it, and it went thump on the pavement underneath, Ruthie and her mother laughed till the tears ran down their faces. When they had finished tidying up, and Ruthie had dragged the mat upstairs again, Ruthie's mother sat down in the armchair by the window, and made a lap for Ruthie.

This was nicest of all. Leon was asleep in his cot in the bedroom, and it was very quiet outside in the street, everyone inside having their dinners away from the heat. Ruthie sat on her mother's lap, and stroked the hand her mother rested on her knees, and sang inside her head.

"It's better like this, Ruthie, schnooky," her mother said. "So it's safer out in the country, but it's better like this, eh?"

"I don't like the country," Ruthie said.

"It's all right for some of them. But for me, I couldn't stand it. What would I do all the time? Better we stay here. If it happens it happens."

"Who puts the names on the bombs, Mummy? Does he have a register like Miss Fletcher, and put names on from that?"

"Names? What names?"

"Mrs Salmon says if a bomb's got your name on it, it's got it, and what can you do? Who puts the names on?"

Ruthie's mother held her very tightly suddenly. "Mrs Salmon was only joking, lovey. She didn't mean it. Just joking."

"Oh." Ruthie couldn't quite see what was funny about

43

bombs with names on them, but if it was a joke, it was, so she laughed.

"When will the bombs stop having names on them?" she asked then.

"When the war's over."

"When will that be? What will we do then?"

"You ask too many questions. Ask, ask, ask! If I knew, I'd tell you. Who knows? I don't."

So Ruthie didn't ask any more questions.

After Leon woke up, they all went down to Black Sophie's shop. Ruthie liked this. The women in the street used to go down to Sophie's shop most afternoons. They would sit in the room at the back of the shop, on kitchen chairs, and the back door to the yard would be open, and they would drink tea and talk, and sometimes when people came into the shop and called out to Black Sophie to come and serve them, Ruthie would go with her, and Black Sophie would let her put the sweets on the weighing machine and count out the money for the change.

Black Sophie's shop was lovely. It was very dark, and there was a counter with a flap you lifted to go through to the room at the back. It smelled of sweets, liquorice and chocolate, and fruit drops, and there were big jars in rows on the shelves, full of sweets and toffees in papers. Best of all, there were piles of pretend boxes of chocolates behind the counter, and Ruthie would sometimes pile them up in heaps and play shops herself, selling the chocolates to people inside her head.

But this afternoon, Ruthie and her mother and Leon

went into the room behind the shop right away, and Black Sophie gave Ruthie a long black ribbon of liquorice, all rolled up flat, with a big red sweet in the middle.

Ruthie looked at her mother when Black Sophie gave her the liquorice, and said, "No, thank you very much," but Black Sophie just laughed and said, "So take it, boobalah! Let her have it, Bessie. I give to all the children, so I shouldn't give to your Ruthie? Let her have it already."

Ruthie's mother frowned slightly.

"I don't want she should grow up to be greedy, Sophie, always looking for what she can get out of people . . ."

Black Sophie laughed, fat and wobbly, her tiny gold ear-rings bobbing against her fat shoulders. She was so fat her neck had sunk into her shoulders and her ears rested right against the black cloth of her dress.

"Please God she should grow up! I tell you, she'll be no shnorrer, your Ruthie. She's a good girl, eh, dolly?"

Ruthie nodded, carefully not looking at the liquorice with its red sweet in the middle. There was something called asking with your eyes, and that was as bad as asking properly, so she didn't look, watching her mother's face all the time.

Mrs Salmon, already sitting in a chair by the table in the back room called out, "So what's the matter with you Mrs Lee? A bit of liquorice to hurt the child? Let her have it!"

45

"All right—all right," Ruthie's mother said. "What do you say, Ruthie?"

"Thank you very much," Ruthie said, and took the liquorice to hold it flat between her two hands so that only the edges showed round her fingers.

"Give me that boychick of yours, Bessie." Black Sophie put her arms out, and Leon looked at her for a minute, peering over his shoulder before putting his head in his mother's neck.

Black Sophie laughed delightedly. "Look at him, the lobbus! Flirting with me yet! Come to Sophie, then, come to Sophie." And she took Leon and he laughed and dribbled at her while she threw him up and down in the air.

"Not too much, Sophie," Ruthie's mother said. "He'll be sick on you."

So Sophie put him down on the floor by the door to the yard, and gave him her big bunch of keys to play with, and Leon put them in his mouth and sat and laughed at the women sitting round.

There were a lot of them this afternoon, Mrs Salmon, and Mrs Coram, and Mrs Marks and Mrs Kaye, whose Rachel was a bit slow, and Mrs Fleischer whose son was going to be a doctor. Mrs Fleischer lived next door to Ruthie, and was always talking about her Lenny who was at the hospital and would be a doctor one day soon. Ruthie liked Lenny a lot. He was a nice man, and whenever she saw him, he tickled her, and called her his best girl, and Ruthie would bend double to get away from his

46

tickling fingers, and think he was wonderful to be going to be a doctor.

"So you goin' out to play, Ruthie?" Mrs Salmon asked. "My Esther she's up the street with the others. You goin' to play with them?"

Ruthie shook her head. "No, thank you, Mrs Salmon. I'll stay here and eat my liquorice."

Mrs Salmon was always telling Ruthie to go and play with her Esther and her friends, but if she ever did, they sent her away because she was too little for their games. They used to play doctors a lot, and being ill, and lie down to be examined, and Ruthie was too young for that, they said, giggling and looking at each other and pushing each other about.

So Ruthie went and sat under the table instead. It was very nice under the table. There was a little hassock that Black Sophie put her feet on when she sat by the table herself, and Ruthie could use it for a table, putting her gas mask on it, and the things she liked to play with on different days. Today it was pencil and a little red book, with a cover that had wriggly shiny patterns on it, and pages with lines on them inside. She arranged these on the hassock, and crossed her legs, and started to unwind the liquorice till the sweet in the middle came out, and the liquorice was a long smooth strap. Then she put the sweet in the middle of a page of her notebook, and drew all round it to make a circle. Then she made another circle, and put lines under them so that they turned into balloons on strings, and then she drew a big fish shape, and put a big tail on it, and put strings under that, so that it was a picture of a barrage balloon.

Barrage balloons were very beautiful and Ruthie wished she had coloured pencils to make the colours that shone all round the outside of barrage balloons on sunny days like today. But she only had her ordinary pencil, and that wouldn't make the colours, so she drew lines on her picture of a barrage balloon instead.

Above her, the voices of the women made a comfortable sound, all talking together, so that what they said got mixed up with each other. Mrs Fleischer was talking about her Lenny, and how he had been working in the hospital in the last big raid, and seen—and then Mrs Salmon said something about her Esther, and it made it sound as though it had been Esther working in the hospital who had seen terrible things, and that made Ruthie laugh softly under the table.

She could see Mrs Salmon's legs right in front of her, the fringe on the edge of Black Sophie's red tablecloth all stringly over her fat knees. Mrs Salmon's legs had big bandages on them, under her thick brown stockings, and the edges of the bandages made a path that went round and round the legs, and she had a hole in the side of one of her blue slippers. Ruthie very carefully put the point of her pencil into the hole, and Mrs Salmon pulled her foot away, but she didn't stop talking, and Ruthie had to put her hand over her mouth to stop herself laughing. Mrs Salmon didn't know Ruthie was there, right in front of her feet, and that was very funny.

Black Sophie's feet were moving about the floor, and Ruthie listened to the swish of water as she filled the kettle, and the loud hiss and pop as she put it on the gas stove, and the clink of cups as she got them out of the dresser to make tea. And then, when the tea was made, and the women were drinking, Ruthie sat very quietly, biting little pieces off the end of her liquorice strap, listening. This was when they talked most, when the tea was made, and Ruthie liked to listen to them, talking about babies, and the people in the street, and the terrible things that happened in the raids. Today they had forgotten she was there—she could tell this, because they were all talking in English. When they knew children were there, and they wanted to say things children shouldn't hear, they talked in Yiddish.

They talked about babies for a while, and Ruthie's mother was saying what happened when Leon was born, how he was so big she thought she would split from top to bottom, and the doctor had said he had never had to put in so many stitches. But Ruthie had heard all that before.

Then Mrs Marks, who had a baby as old as Leon, and a lot of black hair she had in curls on top of her head, said what had happened when her David was born. "But, I tell you, I lie awake even when there's no raid, worrying about what I should do if something should happen to him—after all that suffering, if something should happen to him, I want to die . . ."

"So what should happen to him?" Mrs Salmon's

voice above Ruthie sounded so close that Ruthie thought if she looked up she would be able to see her right through the wood of the table. "He's a fine big boy, and nothing bad should come to him. And if God forbid in a raid—so you're together. Like I always say, so long as you're together, it's all right. He goes, you go. You don't get left to worry about afterwards."

"A raid—this I know about. No—it's the gas masks."

"So he's got one—you got one, he's got one. You put him in his gas mask and you pump." This from Mrs Coram on the other side of the room.

Mrs Marks' voice was very high and whiny like an all-clear. "Sure—so I put him in and I pump the handle. Fine. So what happens if the warning comes late, like it does sometimes? You get the warning and the bombs at the same time, don't you? You got no time to think about what you do—you get the warning, the bombs is falling, and you are running still for the shelter. So, if there is a gas raid like this, and the gas comes the same time as the warning? His mask is so big, who can carry it about with them? And even if I have it right there, tell me what I do first? So I put him in and I start to pump. Sure. So by the time he is in, and I start to pump, the gas is here, I haven't time to put my mask on, and me—no mask on, I get the gas, who pumps for my David?"

"So you put your mask on first," said Mrs Salmon.

"And by the time I have it on, what happens to my David? I should wait to put him in his mask after I put my own on? And he gets the gas . . ." Mrs Marks' voice went higher and whinier than ever.

"There won't be no gas," Mrs Coram said, her voice fat and comfortable. "My Harry, when I write to him about gas, he writes straight back—I shouldn't worry—no gas. He says it can't happen, of this he's sure."

"I wish I could be so sure," Black Sophie said. "Believe me, I wish I could be like your Harry and be so sure. How come he knows so sure? You think the Government they give us all these gas masks for a joke? They got nothing better to do? If they give you gas masks, then you need to have them. They don't give you for nothing so quickly."

"So how can the Government be sure? They give you the masks in case. They don't know."

"Sure they know," Mrs Fleischer said. "Sure they do. You know how it is? I tell you. I talk to my Lenny, and I tell him the same. The Government here, the Government in Germany, they got it all planned. The Germans want to send gas? Sure—so they tell the Government here they should be out of the way, and they send it. This way, the Government is all right, and God help us. We got our gas masks, the Government says, so all right. What they care about us?"

Under the table, Ruthie nodded to herself. Mrs Fleischer must be right, she thought, why else is the Government in Cornwall with the other children from the street?

"You know what I do if God forbid there should be gas and I got no gas mask?" Black Sophie said.

"You got no gas mask?" Mrs Salmon asked. "Why not? You lost it? So you get another right away. You go to the centre, and you get another one . . ."

"Nah—I got one. But if maybe the gas comes when I haven't got it with me? Maybe I'm in the street, or somewhere, and I left it behind? Me—I don't shlap it out with me all the time. I got enough to carry if I go shopping—I can't always carry no gas mask."

"So what you do?"

"I tell you." Ruthie heard Black Sophie put her cup down on the table above her head. "I tell you. I take my handkerchief, right?"

"So? What good is a handkerchief with gas? You think it can keep it out?"

"So let me finish! I take my handkerchief, I fold it so it's just big enough it covers my mouth and my nose, and then . . ." She paused dramatically. "Then, I pee on it, so it's wet all over, and this I clap on my face! This makes a good gas mask you need one when you ain't got one properly."

The other women began to talk, Mrs Salmon laughing loudly, calling Black Sophie a pisher, and under the table Ruthie sat very still, the end of the liquorice she had just put in her mouth held still between her teeth, feeling as though someone had suddenly thrown a bucket of cold water over her, because she couldn't breathe properly. She sat and stared at Mrs Salmon's bandaged legs in front of her, at the fringe of the tablecloth hanging over her knees, at the hole in Mrs Salmon's slipper, at the pattern the sunlight from the open back door was throwing across the linoleum, making little shadows in front of the cracks and bumps in it, and felt her eyes get big and hot.

She tried to see it. She could see Black Sophie out in the street, with people all round her putting gas masks on their faces while the sirens sounded very close, and gas came out of aeroplanes in the sky, hissing and plopping the way gas always did when you first turned the tap on the gas stove and the match blew out, and she could smell the gas coming from the aeroplanes, see the gas stoves inside the aeroplanes making the gas. She could see Mrs Marks in the middle of the street, putting her baby in his big box of a gas mask, then taking him out to put her own on, then taking hers off to put her baby in, while she cried in her high all-clear voice, "So what do I do first?" And there, on the pavement in front of her shop, Black Sophie folding her handkerchief so that it was just big enough to cover her mouth and nose, then lifting her huge black skirts, pulling her knickers down . . .

But she couldn't see the rest. How could she? It had never occurred to Ruthie that grown-ups like Black Sophie ever did what she did—ever made all that water she made herself, ever got wet as Ruthie got wet. She knew her mother went to the lavatory—of course she did—but that was only to do mysterious things with cotton wool, things to do with being grown up. She knew one day, when she was grown up, she would have to use cotton wool like her mother did, would have to burn little packets wrapped in newspaper in the fireplace like her mother did. Her mother had told her when she asked, it was to do with being grown up, and when she was a big girl she would know about it. But did her mother go to the lavatory to do wees like Ruthie did? The whole idea was impossible to Ruthie, sitting there under Black Sophie's table.

But she must do—if Black Sophie did, and the other women weren't surprised that she did, it must mean that they did, too. Mrs Salmon had said Black Sophie was a pisher, but only children were pishers, dirty things who made trouble for their poor mothers, like Ruthie did because she made all that water in her bottom. Were grown-ups pishers, too? Ruthie felt crying climbing up inside her neck. Would it always be the same? She had thought that it was just something that happened now, that when she was grown up, like her mother, it would stop, she would never have to lie and hurt her toes and her lip in bed, never have to pray to God to stop her wetting her bed, never have to sit on hot kerbstones to dry her knickers again. But now she knew. It would never stop. Grown-ups weren't special any more. They were like children, like Ruthie. They made water as well, they could get wet, too. There was nothing left to look forward to.

The crying came to the top of her neck, up to the back

of her eyes, came out of her mouth in a shrill sound, and Ruthie sat under the table, her face screwed up tight, her mouth pulled back by the tears in her neck, hearing the crying loud inside her head as well as coming out of her mouth.

In front of her swimming eyes, the tablecloth moved, the fringe came away from Mrs Salmon's bandaged legs, and Mrs Salmon's face appeared above her fat knees, peering down at Ruthie sitting cross-legged in front of the hassock, the liquorice strap in her hand, her mouth blackened with it, as she howled.

"Oy, nebbish!" Mrs Salmon cried. "What happened? What you doing there?"

She pulled on Ruthie's arm, hauled her out, while still Ruthie cried, tears dripping off the end of her nose.

"What's the matter, dolly? What happened? You bite your tongue?"

All Ruthie could say was, "Gas," the word coming mixed up with her crying and her mother came and picked her up, and held her close.

"I forgot she was there," she said above Ruthie's head, pressing it down onto her shoulder, rocking her in her arms. "God forgive me, I forgot she was there. To talk of such things in front of a child—she's frightened of the gas—to talk of such things before a child."

The other women got up from their chairs, coming round to pat Ruthie where she clung howling to her mother, and even above her tears, she could hear them crying themselves.

"Nebbish, nebbish," Mrs Salmon was saying, her voice all thick. "Poor baby—such times to live in for her. Poor baby—to be so frightened."

"Listen, dolly, we was only joking—only joking. There won't be no gas raids—we forgot you was there —we make jokes—there won't be no gas," Black Sophie said loudly, sniffing as she spoke.

But Ruthie only clung to her mother hopelessly and cried. It didn't help, clinging to her mother. Not a bit. How could it? Her mother, all the others, all the grown-ups in the world, they were pishers like Ruthie. They were no more than children like herself, only big children. To be grown up was nothing any more. She could never trust them again, none of them. The world was a horrible place with nothing but wetness to think of for ever and ever.

CHAPTER FIVE

RUTHIE woke quite suddenly.

The light was on, and across the room her mother was bundling Leon into a blanket, her yellow hair flopping untidily round her face as she moved. Above the sound of the siren, the very close one they always got up for, she could hear the more distant whine of the other sirens, and the big thumping sounds from far away that made her shiver, because the thumps made the house shake very slightly, made Ruthie's feet tickle with the wobble of the house. She knew it wasn't very late, because her mother still had on the dress she had worn all day, with a cardigan over it now, and anyway, she could feel that it was still not the part of the night that was nearly morning. It smelled different when it was nearly morning, like tomorrow, but now it still smelled like today, with the liver that had been fried for supper still in the air.

Her mother went down the stairs first, holding Leon high on one shoulder, peering round him as she picked her way over the cracked lino that covered the steps.

The front door was open, and outside, Ruthie could see Mr Levine on the doorstep in his slippers and with his braces hanging down over his trousers. He was standing with his head thrown back, staring up at the sky, and his hair stood out black against the brightness of a search-light that filled the blackness above the roofs of the houses on the other side of the street. Which was funny, because Mr Levine's hair was white, really.

Ruthie only ever saw Mr and Mrs Levine when there was a raid. Mr Levine went every day to his workshop, where he was a presser, and Mrs Levine went to the workshop too where she was a felling hand, and they never came home at night till Ruthie was in bed.

"Alf!" Mrs Levine came waddling along the passage towards the front door, her big shopping bag, the plaited straw one, in her hand, a big fur coat on, and her hair pulled back under a big black hat with flowers on it. "Alf! What's a matter with you? You want you should be blown to pieces? Come on."

Mr Levine came in, and shut the front door, so that the only light came from the Levines' open kitchen door, at the end of the passage, behind the brown plush curtain that half shut off their end of the hallway. He locked the door carefully, muttering under his breath, while Mrs Levine stood behind him pulling at his shirt sleeve.

"So come on, Alf! The box is all ready, and the gas is turned off—hello, Mrs Lee!" She nodded absently at Ruthie and her mother standing waiting at the bottom of the stairs. "I tell him, all the time I tell him. This is no time to stand admiring the view. But always he looks, always he looks and takes such chances. He wants we should all be blown up? I ask him, but what can you do? Does he listen to me?"

"So I'm coming! I want to see, is that so wrong? They're over the docks. You could go to bed again, believe me, tonight it's the docks . . ."

"Every night it's the docks, only they don't know like we do where the docks finish. Soon they think Aspen Street is the docks, and you stand out there on the step like a shlemiel so they make no mistake when they come and they get Alf Levine! So come on."

Still muttering, Mr Levine led the way down the passage, and Mrs Levine and Ruthie and her mother and Leon followed him. He picked up the big box of photographs, the silver candlesticks, and Mrs Levine's best clothes, and Mr Levine's best Homburg hat, and pushed the back door open, shepherding them out to the yard.

Ruthie liked this door very much. It had a top half made of glass, and over the glass Mrs Levine had stuck waxed paper, all covered in brightly coloured triangles, and over this again had hung a net curtain that had patterns of butterflies in it, all made of strands of yellow cotton.

It was still warm in the yard, the heat of the day lingering in the cracked concrete, round the three battered dustbins that had to be carried through the house passage to the front on the dustmen's day, in the old tin bath that hung from one handle against the wall beside the outside lavatory.

Right in the middle of what had once been the square of the yard, the hump that was the shelter raised itself in the blackness of the hot summer night, with a fringe of grass on the top silhouetted against the searchlights in the sky just as Mr Levine's hair had been.

Mr Levine went into the shelter first, scrabbling about in the dark for the oil lamp, scratching away with matches to light it, while the two women stood close behind him, edging forwards anxiously.

Ruthie stayed on the top step of the three that led down to the shelter, looking up into the sky, her eyes still a little thick with sleep, feeling her cardigan scratching her back through her thin nightgown, curling her toes inside her sandals, enjoying the way the leather rubbed her skin, because she had no socks on.

There were more searchlights than she could count tonight, she saw with admiration, all swooping about too fast to be counted. The thumping was getting louder, closer, with lovely crunchy noises coming right after each thump, sounding as though a huge stall full of giant potatoes were being scooped with an enormous brass scoop, so that the potatoes, bigger than the whole world, tumbled thud, thud, against each other. Ruthie bounced on her toes at the lovely noise. Then there was a big grumbling noise, a noise that Mr Levine had once told her came from the guns down by the docks, a noise like a lot of thunderstorms all at once, and at this Ruthie really jumped up and down, loving the roar and grumble, the way the air trembled and the ground tickled her feet with each long growling burst.

"Ruthie! Come here at once. What's the matter with you—have you gone to sleep?" Her mother was peering up the steps at her, so with a last regretful look up at the beautiful fingers of the searchlights, Ruthie slid down the steps into the shelter.

Their shelter wasn't as nice as some of the shelters in Aspen Street. The one next door was lovely, Ruthie thought. In Mrs Fleischer's shelter, there was a little table and a bench to sit on, as well as two bunk beds like those in the Levines' shelter, and the camp bed they kept pushed under the bunks. But Mrs Fleischer didn't have a cupboard like the Levines', a cupboard full of tins of biscuits and sugar and tea and cups and saucers. They kept all their things like that in a box under their table, with a big white tablecloth on the table to hide what was underneath. Mrs Fleischer had a piece of carpet on the floor of their shelter, but the Levines just had the old sacks Mr Levine had bought from the potato stall.

"I should waste good money putting carpets on a shelter floor, yet?" he had shouted at Mrs Levine one night, when she had complained about the poorness of their shelter compared with others in the street. "So I'm a lunatic or something? Carpets I buy for houses, not for shelters."

There was a shelf up on one side of the shelter, fastened to the corrugated iron with big brackets, and on this the big old oil lamp stood burning brightly. Mr Levine was very proud of this lamp, and always reminded his wife, every time they used the shelter, that it had been because of what she was pleased to call his miserliness that they had such an excellent light in their shelter. The lamp, made of brass and with a high glass chimney and a round milky globe with flowers engraved on it, had belonged to his mother, and all through their married life, when Mrs Levine had tried to persuade him to throw it out together with the rest of the junk Mr Levine treasured so jealously, he had refused. Ruthie had heard him talk about his refusal so often that she felt sometimes as though she had been there all the time, whenever they had argued about the junk Mr Levine kept in their front room.

As soon as Ruthie was inside the shelter, Mr Levine pulled the big door closed, shutting out the searchlights and the lovely noise. Mrs Levine was already on the bottom bunk, her legs stuck awkwardly in front of her, her plaited bag on her lap.

"So are you going to be all night getting ready?"

The familiar pattern of nights in the shelter began, with Mr and Mrs Levine bickering, sometimes loudly, sometimes in furious half-whispers, while Ruthie's mother, her face closed and grim, lay in silence, reading a magazine or a book she had borrowed from the library.

Mr Levine with exasperating slowness pulled the camp bed out from under the bottom bunk, and Ruthie's mother jerked her head at Ruthie, who came obediently to climb under the scratchy blankets on it. As she settled herself, her mother climbed onto the other end, pushing Ruthie to one side with her feet, arranging the sleeping Leon in the crook of her arm, while Mr Levine, with much grunting, climbed up to the top bunk, to lie on his back, his nose nearly touching the corrugations of the roof.

Mrs Levine, twisting and turning on her bunk like an angry cat, keeping her hat on even while she was lying down, arranged her plaited straw bag carefully at her side, and settled down to talk the raid away. Ruthie's mother arranged a book, holding it uncomfortably in the hand of the arm that was round Leon, propping her head up on the one thin striped pillow on the camp bed squirting at the print in the soft yellow glow of the lamplight.

Ruthie lay and stared up at the curved roof above her, careful not to fidget, because that always made her mother angry, and tried not to listen to Mrs Levine's monotonous voice, trying to hear the thumps and roars from outside.

It was easy to hear them tonight, because they sounded very close, and once a very loud crump made the lamp on the shelf sway, so that they all looked at it, keeping very still, frightened to move in case their movement should send it crashing down. But it straightened itself, only a blur of lampblack on the chimney left to show what had happened.

Ruthie fell asleep quite abruptly, in the middle of a

very long roar from the guns, the light inside her eyes from the lamp suddenly fading away to blackness.

When she woke, the lamp was out, and she could hear Mr Levine breathing thickly from somewhere above her in the darkness, and Leon whimpering a little, wriggling somewhere near her feet.

Then she heard it again, the high wail of the all-clear that had woken her, and she moved slightly, whispering "Mummy?" carefully wriggling her feet away from her mother's side. She was wet again, of course, but in the shelter, somehow that didn't seem to matter so much. As long as the wetness didn't reach her mother, Ruthie knew she was safe.

Above her, Mr Levine stirred, muttered, and then Mrs Levine woke, calling petulantly, "So open up, Alf! Are you deaf? The all-clear—open up."

They came blinking out into the early morning sunlight, and Ruthie took a deep breath as she came to the top step, surprised as always to find how different it smelled outside, how thick the smell in the shelter had been. But this morning the smell was quite different, not thin and clean like usually, but heavy with smoke. Her mother came up the steps to come to where Ruthie was standing beside Mr Levine. He was standing quite still, making no attempt to go to the house and open the back door as he usually did, his head up as he sniffed.

"What's happened?" Mrs Levine came panting up the steps, her flowered hat twisted on her grey hair. "What is it—the house?"

It all looked the same everywhere, their house, the houses each side of them, the yard with its dustbins and cracked concrete.

"Nah." Mr Levine was quiet. "All right this side—but it smells bad—I'll go see."

They followed him into the house, Leon whimpering, Ruthie painfully aware of the wetness of her nightdress under her cardigan. The house looked the same, until they went through the curtain in the passage, and Mr Levine opened the door of the front room.

He stood there, both hands holding his cheeks, staring round at the piled furniture, the heaps of old clothes he kept in one corner, the boxes of old newspapers and magazines. Ruthie came and looked under his arm, and stared too.

The window was gone, the glass lying in shattered sparkling heaps under the sill, everything covered in whitish powder, and above, a big piece of the ceiling was gone, only a patch of bare wooden joists showing through the hole.

Mrs Levine started to cry as soon as she saw the mess, rocking her body backwards and forwards, making ineffectual dabs at the powdery mess on the lino with one foot, until Mr Levine turned and said viciously, "So shut up! So there's a mess! It'll kill you to clean it up, will it? So get a broom!"

As soon as she saw the mess in the Levine's front room, Ruthie's mother turned and hurried up the stairs, to see what had happened there, and Ruthie ran after her.

The place above the Levine's front room was the hallway outside Ruthie's mother's kitchen. Ruthie looked from behind her mother when they got to the top of the stairs, full of hope.

There was glass all over the floor, but no powdery whiteness—the ceiling here was just as usual. Ruthie moved forwards to pick up some of the long pieces of glass that shone so beautifully in the sunlight, but her mother pulled her back with a painful twist of her arm.

"Keep back—the floor might go. I'll clear it myself."

So Ruthie went into the kitchen, but to her intense disappointment everything here was all right. No broken glass, no powder on the furniture, everything as usual. Her eyes filled with tears as she looked. She so much wanted a piece of the sparkling broken glass, but how could she get it? If her mother wouldn't let her go into the hallway to get a piece because of the floor, and Mrs Levine was crying so embarrassingly downstairs what could she do?

Her mother looked at her sharply, and then said with the warm voice that Ruthie liked to hear, "Never mind, lovey—it's all right, you see? Nothing broken here. We're lucky, aren't we?" and though Ruthie didn't think so at all, she nodded, swallowing her tears, and smiling at her mother as best she could.

Talking all the time, her mother bustled about, dressing her and Leon, washing her face at the sink in the corner, making breakfast of bread and cream cheese and tea, feeding Leon's wide mouth full of bread and milk, while Ruthie sat silent at the table thinking about the way the glass downstairs and in the hallway had sparkled, and how much she would have liked a piece to keep for herself.

She was nearly finished with her breakfast before she noticed the way her mother was trying to keep between her and the window. Something she doesn't want me to see, thought Ruthie, and with a sharp glance at her mother, decided that her mood was the sort that would mean she could go and look and not be smacked for it. So she slipped from her seat quickly while her mother was bending over Leon, giving him a drink of milk from a cup, and ran to the window.

It was funny. Across the street, there was a gap, just like the gap in her mother's teeth. There had always been a row of houses all joined together, only now Mrs Levy's house, and the ones on each side, were gone, just gone. There was a big pile of bricks and grey stones, with people in tin hats walking around on it, but no houses.

Ruthie stared, excited, forgetting her sadness about the glass she couldn't have. The pile of bricks and stones on the other side was much more promising, and as soon as she could, she thought, she would go and see what she could get from the pile for herself.

Her mother came and stood beside her, and said gently, "It was a bomb, Ruthie. It—it broke Mrs Levy's house."

Ruthie nodded, enthralled.

"Look—there's a bed on that pile of stones—see?

With all those bricks over it—and all the blankets are on it, can you see, Mummy? Can you see all the blankets on it?" The bed looked very funny, Ruthie thought it was funny, too. But her mother's face was very straight, so Ruthie didn't laugh.

"Don't watch, Ruthie. Come away from the window—don't look. They'll clear it up soon—don't watch."

"But I want to."

"No!" her mother said violently. "Do you hear me? I said no! When they've cleared up everything, then you can go out—but God help you if you move out of this room till I say you can, do you hear?"

So for the rest of the day, Ruthie stayed in the kitchen, while the sun got hotter and hotter, aching to go out but not daring to. Her mother went in and out of the kitchen, busily clearing the mess in the hallway, fixing pieces of wood across the floor over the place where the ceiling downstairs had a hole in it, but even when she was out of the room, Ruthie knew better than to dare to look out of the window. She had a feeling her mother would know if she did, and that would mean a row.

Late in the afternoon, while Ruthie was drawing in her red book again, making pictures of aeroplanes with big bombs in them, she heard voices below the window, one of them her mother's.

It wouldn't do to look out of the window, but that didn't mean she couldn't listen to what was going on, so she carefully slid across the room to sit on the floor under it, and listened.

Mrs Fleischer and Mrs Coram were talking to her mother, and Ruthie could almost see the look of smugness on Mrs Fleischer's face as she said, "My Lenny —all night he was working—only a student he is, but last night he work like a real doctor already. I put him to bed a half an hour ago—I tell you, that boy is exhausted, worn out he is. A day and a night he works with no sleep, nebbish."

"Have they got her out yet?" That was her mother.

"Sure—dinner time they got her out. Terrible it was —the A.R.P. man told me, nothing of her left, he said."

"God rest her soul," Mrs Coram said. "God rest her soul. I told her, times and times I told her, the shelter is there, you should use it, but Mrs Levy—you know Mrs Levy, rest her soul. Always under the stairs she sits. She don't go to no shelter, she says, they're dirty places. Under my own clean stairs, there I'm all right, she says. A terrible thing."

"Thank God no one else . . ." Ruthie's mother said. "Where are they—the others? The Karminskys, the Steins?"

"The centre—the Commercial Road centre. Where they go after that I don't know. Maybe they go away to the country now—who knows?"

"You should take your Ruthie and Leon and go to the country, Mrs Lee." This was Mrs Fleischer. "Me, I stay here for my Lenny. He got to work at the hospital, so I got to stay look after him. Always he says, Momma, go to the country, but me, I tell him. You work at the hospital, Lenny, so I stay, I look after you. Can I leave a boy alone here? But you, Mrs Lee—you should go. For the children."

"And what about Benny?" Her mother's voice sounded very hard to Ruthie, sitting under the window listening. "How do I go and Benny won't know where we are? When he comes back, then maybe . . ."

"So listen, Mrs Lee. You think he'll come back here? Don't he know the army are looking for him? Always they send men to ask you, is Benny here? You think he don't know this? Sure he knows. He won't come back here—maybe he'll write you a letter, but he don't come back. So you go to the country, you tell the postman where you goin' and he sends Benny's letter to you when he writes . . ."

"I stay here," Ruthie's mother said flatly. "I've got to talk to him before the army gets him back—my God, have I got to talk to him. . . ."

Ruthie slid away from the window. When they started to talk about her father like this, it was time to stop listening. So when her mother came upstairs again to give her her supper and put her to bed, she was sitting at the table, drawing pictures of soldiers with white hats on, and big boots.

CHAPTER SIX

———

EVERYTHING seemed to get a lot nicer after Mrs Levy was killed in the raid. No one else in the street had been killed before, and Ruthie was very proud of this. She told Mrs Ward about it when she went to school in the morning, very excitedly, and Mrs Ward had shivered and closed her eyes for a moment before talking to Ruthie about something else, and Ruthie felt very pleased about this. It wasn't everyone who knew someone who had been killed like she had known Mrs Levy, and Mrs Ward was obviously impressed. If she hadn't been, she wouldn't have tried to pretend she hadn't heard properly.

Everyone in Aspen Street got a lot friendlier, too, even her mother. Now when Mrs Cohen gave her biscuits or Black Sophie called her over—"You want a sweetie, dolly? So come to Sophie—I got sweeties for you. Come and get, dolly"—her mother made no attempt to stop her from taking the things. Ruthie ate a lot of sweets and biscuits.

There were big raids nearly every night, now, and

most afternoons as well, though the afternoon ones weren't very big ones—sometimes they weren't in the shelter more than a half hour or so.

School was very nice too. She went most mornings, even after big raids, because her mother said it would take her mind off things, though Ruthie wasn't quite sure what she meant when she said that. At school, they played a lot, and sang a lot, and did P.T. a lot, and Mrs Ward gave the children sweets as well. Some days, what with the sweets from Mrs Ward and the biscuits and sweets from Mrs Cohen and Black Sophie, Ruthie had enough sweets to swop as well as to eat. She got ten coloured pencils from one girl at school, and three books, big annuals, from a big boy, and a lovely bird with real feathers on it that you wound up with a key, and then it walked about and made cheeping noises. She lost the key to that, after a few days, so she swopped it for a big drawing-book with thick pages in it. Ruthie was very happy about this.

Of course, there was still the trouble with the wet beds at night, and when she went to sleep on the camp bed in the shelter, her mother made her wrap up in an old macintosh, so that the wetness didn't go over her and Leon, and the macintosh smelled nasty, and made her very hot and itchy, but she got used to it.

One afternoon, a week or so after Mrs Levy had been killed, Ruthie was playing in the street with a ball. It was a very nice ball, with yellow and red and green and blue on it, all mixed up together in swirly stripes, and when Ruthie bounced it, all the colours shivered together and looked very beautiful. She was trying to do One Two Three Alairy, My ball went down the airy, lifting her leg over the ball between bounces. Lilian was very good at this, and Ruthie was practising it a lot, though it was very difficult. On the third try, the ball hit the edge of the kerb, and went rolling very quickly along the street towards Mrs Cohen's. She ran after it, and caught it just by the way into the alleyway that led to Festival Street.

It was always a bit dark in the alleyway, and cool, and Ruthie looked along it because she liked the way the light at the other end sparkled against the dimness of the alleyway walls. She could see the four big girls there, Mrs Salmon's Esther, and Rachel Kaye, who was a bit slow, and Shirley and Sandra who were sisters. They were standing very close together, and they were giggling and pushing each other about the way they did when they were playing doctors and told Ruthie she was too little to play with them.

Ruthie looked at them, and thought it would be nice to play with them today. Lilian didn't play with her as much as she had once, not since the day she had spat at Ruthie, because Ruthie was a bit frightened she would spit again, and Lilian seemed to know Ruthie was frightened and was nasty to her.

So Ruthie walked into the alleyway, holding her ball, and came to stand next to the girls. They took no notice of her, because there was someone else there they were looking at while they giggled and pushed at each other.

It was a man, someone Ruthie hadn't ever seen before. He was a tall man, thin, with a bent back, and his face had a lot of pimples on it. He had thin fair hair, not a nice yellow like Lilian's or Ruthie's mother after she had used the toothbrush on it, but a thin pale sort of colour, all flat, without any shine on it, and it hung over his eyes. His mouth was a bit open, and stretched in a funny sort of way, not exactly a smile, not exactly like the way your mouth stretched when you were trying not to cry, but a bit of each.

He was standing with his hands in front of him, fiddling with something Ruthie couldn't see properly, something that looked greyish in the dim light of the alleyway, and Ruthie moved forwards a bit so that she could see properly. But she still couldn't understand what he was doing; all she could see was that he had unbuttoned the front of his trousers, and whatever it was he was holding was part of his trousers, or so it looked.

And then Esther giggled again, a breathless sort of giggle that sounded bubbly as though it came from her throat, and Ruthie moved her eyes away from the man and looked at her. Esther had very big black eyes, with very long eyelashes, and her eyes were the sort that stuck out a bit. They were shining now, shining in the dark alleyway, and her mouth was half open, and looked wet, as though she had just licked her lips. Her face was flushed, and there was a sort of glassy look in her shiny eyes that made Ruthie feel very frightened suddenly.

So she looked away from Esther's face at the others. But they were the same, all staring at the man's hands and trousers, all with the wet look on their mouths, all very bright-eyed. Only Rachel looked a bit different, Rachel whose mouth always hung open a bit, who behaved like a baby sometimes though she was thirteen last birthday. Rachel was swaying backwards and forwards, very evenly, her eyes never leaving the man's hands. Looking at her, Ruthie felt suddenly very frightened indeed. She wanted to turn and run away up the alley, back to the sunshine of Aspen Street to play One Two Three Alairy again, but she couldn't go on her own, couldn't turn her back on the four girls, in case they looked at her with those horrible shiny eyes, in case they followed her and giggled in her ear with that horrible bubbly giggle. So she stood very still, staring at the four girls, taking no notice of the man leaning against the wall with his hands in front of him and his trousers all unbuttoned.

And then Rachel moved forwards towards the man, her eyes all flat and shiny, and put her hand out towards him. The man made a funny squeaking noise in his throat, and pushed himself back against the wall as though he were frightened of her, too, like Ruthie, and this time, Ruthie couldn't stay, even if by turning her back on the girls it meant they would look at her. She ran up the alleyway as fast as she could, feeling her mouth go stiff and stretched the way it did when she tried not to cry, holding her ball very hard in her hand.

Mrs Cohen was outside her shop as she came bursting

out of the alleyway, fixing another tin of broken biscuits on the shelf in front of the shop window, and when Ruthie came near to her, she stared at her, and dropping the biscuit tin, grabbed at her with one fat hand.

"So, Ruthie, whatsa matter? What happened? You look like you seen a ghost or somethin'. Whatsa matter?"

Ruthie stared up at the friendly face above her, and tried to pull her arm away, twisting against Mrs Cohen's grip, but she couldn't.

"Nothing—nothing, let me go—it's nothing!"

Mrs Cohen shook her slightly. "You don't look like that for nothing, boobalah—so what's the matter? What is it?"

And now Ruthie started to cry, the tears all hot on her face, as she twisted against Mrs Cohen's strong hand.

"It's nothing—nothing. . . ." Then above her own tears she heard Esther's bubbly giggle again, and she looked over her shoulder at the entrance to the alleyway, terrified in case the girls would come out and look at her with their shiny eyes and wet mouths, and she wriggled harder than ever, crying very loudly.

Mrs Cohen went to the top of the alleyway herself to look down it, pulling Ruthie with her, and peered along into the dimness.

"Something in Festival Street is it, boobalah?" she said, and then suddenly let go of Ruthie's arm to run awkwardly up the alleyway towards the girls and the tall man with the flat fair hair.

Ruthie couldn't do anything now but stand still and

cry, the tears running down her face. There was a noise in the alleyway, Mrs Cohen's voice very loud and echoing so that you couldn't hear exactly what she was shouting, the girls suddenly bursting into loud shrieks as though they were crying too. Then there was a clatter as the man ran away, back along the alley to the Festival Street end, and Mrs Cohen came out of the alley pushing the girls in front of her.

The noise from the alleyway had brought people from along the street hurrying up to see what was the matter, and Ruthie was suddenly in the middle of a lot of women all talking at the tops of their voices, all shouting at Mrs Cohen to tell them what was the matter, while the girls stood in a cluster, all crying very loudly except Rachel, who stood still and lumpish, her mouth hanging open as usual, her head thrust forwards as she stared round blinking at the women.

"It's all right, boobalah," Mrs Cohen was saying to Esther, who was crying loudest of all, rubbing her eyes with her knuckles. "It's all right—I find your mother. It's all right . . ."

Mrs Salmon came pushing through the little knot of people, her face full of fright, and grabbed at Esther, who immediately threw herself on her broad chest, and clung to her.

"Mummy, Mummy! It was awful, Mummy—it was awful! He wouldn't let us go—it was awful—he was dirty, Mummy, he was dirty . . ."

"So tell me, Esther baby, tell me—what happened?"

77

Mrs Salmon held on tightly to her Esther, stroking her hair with one hand while she mopped at her eyes with an end of her apron. "Tell Momma then, what happened? Who was dirty? What happened?"

Esther, gulping and breathing unevenly so that her words came jerkily, looked up at her mother with a pathetic look on her face, and said piteously, "It was a—a man, Mummy, and he—he—did dirty things . . ."

Mrs Salmon looked very frightened and began to shake Esther urgently.

"He did dirty things to you? A man? Gevult! What did he do, baby—he touched you? What did he do, where did he touch you?"

Esther dropped her eyes in the way Ruthie had seen her drop them at school when Mrs Ward asked which of the children had broken something, and said very quietly, "He—he didn't touch us, Mummy—he showed us—he unbuttoned . . ." She looked at her mother's face through her eyelashes, and started to cry again. "He showed us! He was dirty, Mummy, he was dirty."

The women began to chatter excitedly again, and Ruthie, her own tears drying on her face, stared at Esther and the other girls.

It's all wrong, she thought. It wasn't like that at all. The man was frightened as well, he *was*. Ruthie remembered the man's face, half smiling, half not smiling, and she knew he had been frightened, remembered the funny noise he had made in his throat when Rachel had put her hand out, how he had tried to get further back into the wall away from her, and she stared at Esther and her pretty face and shiny eyes, still a bit shiny like they had been in the alleyway, though shiny with crying as well, and she felt very frightened of Esther.

Esther looked at her for a moment, and Ruthie looked away quickly. She couldn't look at Esther looking at her, it was too awful to see those shiny eyes fixed on her own.

Mrs Salmon took Esther away then, her arm round her shoulders while Esther leaned on her mother and sniffed loudly, and Shirley and Sandra went away with their mother as well, both crying, but looking sideways at Esther as they went, and to Ruthie it was almost as though they giggled at each other and pushed each other with their eyes. Mrs Cohen took Rachel into her shop, because her mother wasn't there—she worked in a workshop some days, and Mrs Cohen kept an eye on Rachel for Mrs Kaye, and Ruthie went back home herself.

Her mother hadn't been in the street when the noise in the alleyway started, and Ruthie was very glad. She hadn't come to see what had happened, so Ruthie didn't have to explain to her mother about it. How could she have explained about the frightened man standing in the alleyway with his hands in front of him, who had been frightened when Rachel put her hand out towards him? She couldn't explain, any more than she could explain about the way Esther's and Sandra's and Shirley's eyes had been shiny, and how they had giggled with a bubbly giggle.

So when she went upstairs, she just asked her mother

if she could stay in and play with Leon, because it was too hot to play outside, and her mother said she could. Ruthie was very glad. She was afraid that if she stayed out, Esther and Sandra and Shirley and Rachel would come out again, and Ruthie was very frightened of them. She never wanted to play with them ever, even if they would let her.

CHAPTER SEVEN

AFTER the day when she sat under Black Sophie's table and discovered that grown-ups were only big children, not better or cleverer than herself, only older, and the business with the frightened man and the four girls in the alleyway, things changed for Ruthie. She didn't know how they had changed—just that she was a different Ruthie.

It wasn't only that she was bigger than she used to be, that her dresses didn't reach as far down her legs as they had, that she needed new sandals because her toes hit the bottom of her old ones. It was more than that. She suddenly knew she was Ruthie, that no one else in the whole world was her, that although people, grown-ups and other children, were like her in lots of ways, no one could be Ruthie but Ruthie.

She would sit on the kerb outside her house, looking at her legs where they came out of her dress, at the faint bluish circles in the skin under the brownness of the tan she had developed from the day-in, day-out, heat of the sun. She would look at her legs, at the skin of her hands, the network of the very tiny lines with golden hairs showing where the lines met each other, and think about being Ruthie.

"This is me," she would say softly, enjoying feeling her lips move against her teeth as she mouthed the words. "This will always be me. I'll get bigger and bigger, and it will always be me. I am Ruthie Lee. Ruthie Lee. I have black hair and brown eyes and I am Ruthie Lee. I have two legs and two eyes and two arms and two thumbs on two hands, and I am Ruthie Lee."

She liked the thought of being special like this, being just herself, most of the time.

Sometimes, though, she would remember the way the four big girls had giggled and looked shiny-eyed and wet-mouthed in the alleyway, and then she didn't like being Ruthie, because it meant that one day, quite soon, when she was as big as they were, she would be like that. For she knew she would, knew she would get excited inside when people did things like the man in the alley-way had done, would feel bubbly inside as the four girls had done. It was strange how she knew, strange as knowing one day she would be big. But she knew, all right.

The hot days pleated themselves into weeks, and Ruthie could recognise how long she had been in Aspen Street, how long since she had left the country.

She still couldn't remember what had happened in the country, just that she had been there, that she had been a problem child, had run away from the country. She knew because she had been told so, but however hard she tried, she couldn't see, inside her head, what the country had looked like. She could see the house they used to live in, before the war, she could see that all right. It had had a kitchen and a living room, and she had had her own bedroom, and there had been no Leon, and Daddy had been there, and Mummy had been there, a different Mummy, friendly, talking more than this one did. But she couldn't see the country at all.

The old Ruthie, the one who had lived in that house, she had not been able to know about time. There had only been now, and there had been then. But the new Ruthie was cleverer. She knew when yesterday was, what had happened yesterday, when last Tuesday had been, and the things that had happened on Tuesday, and this was rather special. It was part of being bigger, of knowing that tomorrow and next Tuesday and the Tuesday after were real, that they would arrive, and that Ruthie would be growing all the time.

Up to now, Ruthie hadn't thought very much about the place she was in. There was home, and when she was there, that was the only place in the world. And there was school, and when she was there, home disappeared and would only come back when Ruthie went there again. Now, she liked to think about where she was. She would draw little pictures of where she was in her red notebook. She would draw Commercial Road, and then draw Aspen Street, with the alleyway at the end, and then Festival Street. Then she would draw a picture of the map of England round the drawings of the streets, with the Government down in Cornwall with the other children. She made a big circle round the streets, and that was London. These drawings were very important to Ruthie, because now she knew where she was.

She was happy. Even when her mother got angry with her for wetting herself, or in the mornings when her bed was wet, she didn't care. Inside herself, while she looked at her mother shouting at her, she would feel happy, because she knew all the time that it didn't matter what her mother said any more, not now Ruthie knew her mother was just a big person called Mrs Lee who got wet herself. This was a secret, of course, that she knew. She wouldn't have told her mother she knew, not for anything. She could look at her shouting, and think, "It doesn't matter, because I know and you don't know I do." It was wonderful.

Ruthie would listen to the women talking in the street, during the long hot afternoons, leaning against the doorway behind her mother's kitchen chair, or in Black Sophie's kitchen, and listen to them talking. They always talked the same way. About babies, about the bombing, about going to the country, about how hard it was to buy things sometimes, and underneath their talking, Ruthie could feel them all tight and frightened. It was as though they had two voices, Ruthie thought sometimes, the ones they talk with, and the ones they think with, and I can hear the thinking voices though they don't know.

She knew what they were frightened of. They were frightened of the bombs, mostly, of getting killed. This was something Ruthie quite understood—that they were frightened. She was often frightened herself, of things like being caught taking an apple from the stall in Festival Street when the stall keeper was asleep in her chair, of Mrs Ward catching her picking her nose—these things. But she couldn't really understand why they were frightened of raids, of being bombed and killed, of having their houses broken. The raids were so exciting—not frightening a bit, just exciting. The rumbling and thumping that made the houses shake, the lovely sweep of the searchlights, these were beautiful, and Ruthie couldn't really see why anyone should be frightened of them. And even if a bomb did break a house, what did it matter? There would be lovely pieces of sparkling broken glass, drifts of white powder everywhere, beds on top of piles of stones. These were lovely things—not frightening ones.

And then something happened that made Ruthie begin to see, just a little bit, why the women in the street were frightened of the beautiful raids. She discovered that raids weren't just beautiful, just sweeping searchlights, and shivery feelings in the ground when the thumps and growls came. Raids could make things happen that were frightening.

It was five o'clock one afternoon. Ruthie was sitting

by the table in the kitchen, rolling a piece of plasticine into a pudding, putting the point of her pencil into the warm plasticine to make a pudding with raisins in it, while her mother was getting things ready for Leon's supper.

"The milk's gone off," Ruthie's mother said, holding the dripping bottle in her hand, crouching over the bowl of water in the corner where she kept the milk to keep it cool. "It's gone off . . ."

"Will you make cream cheese?" Ruthie said, pleased. She liked that, when the sour milk was put in a little muslin bag, and hung over the sink from the tap, dripping softly. She could touch the plump bag, and extra water would drip out, and the place where her finger touched sprang back all smooth as soon as she took her finger away. "Will you make cream cheese?"

"I'll have to. Look, Ruthie, go ask Mrs Fleischer to let me have some milk for the baby—tell her this has gone off, will you? And be quick."

So Ruthie went and asked Mrs Fleischer, but she hadn't any to spare, and she asked Black Sophie, too, and she only had some tinned milk, and the baby wouldn't take that.

Her mother muttered under her breath when Ruthie came back and told her no one had any milk to spare, so Ruthie said, "I'll go to the dairy, shall I? I'll buy some for you."

Ruthie's mother looked at her, her face worried and

said, "It's getting late—there may be a siren soon. . . ."
There often were sirens at this time of day.

"I'll run all the way," Ruthie said. "I'll be quick."
The dairy was in Commercial Road, past the beginning
of Festival Street, quite a long way away.

"I don't think . . ." Ruthie's mother said, then frowned
again when Leon began to cry in the bedroom. "Look,
you'll have to—but God help you if you dawdle, you
hear me? Run all the way . . ."

"I could go across Mrs Levy's," Ruthie said, trying
to be helpful. "That would be quicker."

The gap across the street where Mrs Levy's house had
been made a quick way through to the bottom of Festival
Street, to Commercial Road, and some of the women who
lived in the street did climb awkwardly over the piles of
stones and bricks when they wanted to get to Commercial Road in a hurry. But Ruthie's mother had been furious
the only time Ruthie had gone over there herself, had
promised to give her the hiding of her life if she ever
went there again.

"No!" she said now, very angrily. "No—that's
dangerous. You dare to put foot on that way, and I'll
kill you, you hear me?"

Leon was crying very loudly now, so Ruthie nodded
quickly and said, "I won't then, I promise, God's honour,
I won't. I'll go the proper way, and I'll run."

So her mother gave her a shilling, and Ruthie ran
down the stairs to go to the dairy. She ran all the way to
the end of Aspen Street, because she knew her mother

was watching her from the window, even without turning her head to look. She even ran part of the way along Commercial Road, too, but then she had to stop and walk because she got breathless.

She loved Commercial Road. It was so wide, so full of huge buses and cars and lorries, so full of people rushing about. And there were so many shops to look at, bakers, and grocers, dress shops, and toy shops. There had been a Woolworth's once, before the really big raid that afternoon when the docks got a hell of a pasting. She had heard Lenny Fleischer talking about that day, telling the women how so many people had been in Woolworth's that afternoon that they hadn't been able to get them all out. They had sealed up the place, Lenny said, leaving all the bodies there till they could try to get them out another time. Ruthie had thought then that the people in Woolworth's that afternoon had been very lucky, to be locked in, to be able to take anything they wanted from the counters, until she remembered they were dead, and would be lying down, and couldn't take things from the counters after all.

She didn't stop to look at any of the shops, now. She had promised, and anyway, her mother would be sure to know if she did stop, because she would be a long time. So she went to the dairy as fast as she could.

There was an old man in the dairy, buying milk, and he took a long time to get the money for it from his pocket, so Ruthie stood and waited, enjoying the coolness of the blue and white tiled walls, the thick milky

88

smell, the way the big square of butter at the back of the counter was ridged and bumpy with patterns on it. She wished she was buying butter, so that she could watch the woman in the dairy cut a piece off the big lump with her wooden butter patters, slap the lump from side to side till it was a little square with ridges on it too, from the ridges on the wet wood of the butter patters.

At last the old man went off, holding his bottle of milk close in his hands in front of him, muttering under his breath the way old men always did, like Mr Lipshitz from Aspen Street did whenever Ruthie saw him.

"A pint of milk, please," Ruthie said, and took the big bottle carefully, holding it from the bottom, not round the top where the stopper with its metal pieces to hold it in place was. If you held it there, it could slip out of your hands.

The woman gave her the change. And then, as Ruthie turned to go, the faint sound of the siren started, coming into the cool dairy from the sunny street outside like a soft wind.

"'Ere." The woman behind the counter leaned over and tried to catch at Ruthie. "'Ere, ducks, you'd better stop along of me—come on, ducky, come down the shelter . . ."

"No." Ruthie evaded her clutching hand. "No—I got to go home—Mummy says I got to hurry . . ."

"The siren's gone, for Chrissake! Come on—your mum'll know you've gone down a shelter." The woman was grabbing at things from behind the counter, her handbag and gas mask, and heading for the back of the shop, but Ruthie shook her head.

"No," she said. "Leon's waiting for the milk—he was crying already when I came out—I got to run all the way . . ."

In the street outside, people were running, and already there weren't many left, already most of them had disappeared. Ruthie ran as fast as she could, feeling a lump in her neck because she was frightened. The siren had gone, and her mother would be so angry because she had dawdled, because she hadn't got home before the siren went, so she ran as fast as she could, till her chest felt full and very tight.

One or two people tried to catch her as she ran past them, tried to take her to shelters they were going to, but Ruthie dodged past them and ran on.

And then, as she reached the bottom of Festival Street, she had to stop running because her chest felt so tight. She could see, along the curve of Festival Street, the gap that was the back of where Mrs Levy's house had been, could just see the tops of the houses in Aspen Street, almost see her own house. It would be much quicker to go that way, she thought, almost crying with the pain in her chest from running so fast, but Mummy said I mustn't—and I promised God's honour . . .

And then there was a sudden rumble and crump from behind her, the sort of rumble that made the ground shake, and now Ruthie got really frightened, knowing how angry her mother would be because she hadn't got home sooner, and without thinking about it any more she plunged along Festival Street for the gap where Mrs Levy's house had been.

The crumps and rumbles got louder, the pavement shaking under her feet more than she had ever known it to, so that she almost fell, but she clutched the milk tighter, and ran on.

The stones were piled higher on this side of the gap than on the Aspen Street side, and Ruthie nearly dropped the milk as she clambered up them, her sandals slipping on the loosely piled bricks catching her toes as she struggled over them.

And then, just as a really huge crump came, sounding as though it was right underneath her feet, she tripped. She wasn't sure whether she tripped, or whether it was the crump and the trembling of the ground, but she fell headlong, hitting her head on a big piece of wood as she fell, scraping the side of her leg from knee to ankle so that it felt as though she had burned it.

She rolled as she fell, still clutching the milk with one hand, terrified it would break while she tried to catch at the big piece of wood that had hit her head. But the wood only came with her and she landed heavily on a sharp piece of stone with the wood across her middle. Stones and bricks and dust came tumbling down on top of the wood, clattering round her head, filling up the sides of the little cleft she had fallen into, and still loud roars and crumps came crashing from all round, so that everything shook and trembled furiously.

And then, gradually, it stopped, the crumps and noises, the trembling, seeming to move further away, coming only as distant rumbles of thunder, and Ruthie opened her eyes, which she had shut because all the dust was getting in them, and tried to see what had happened.

She was lying on her back in the hole, the big piece of wood still across her middle, with stones and bricks on each side of her head, over her face, balanced on each other. She could just see, out of one eye, the sky above her, but on the other side she could see nothing. Her leg hurt where she had scraped it, and she tried to move it, to pull herself up, but the piece of wood was too heavy for her. And then she discovered that there were stones and bricks all round her arms as well, all over the bottle of milk, all round her neck so that she couldn't move at all, except for opening and closing her eyes.

She was stuck in a hole on the gap where her mother had said she mustn't go, and the baby was waiting for his milk, crying all the time, and Ruthie had dawdled so that she hadn't got home in time. And she was very frightened indeed, just as frightened as she had been the day the market woman had caught her taking an apple and had threatened to tell her mother about it.

CHAPTER EIGHT

———

THE high wail of the all-clear woke her up. For a moment she couldn't think where she was, what had happened to her bed, and she lay blinking her eyes, looking upwards, trying to remember.

The sky that she could see with one eye was a softer deeper blue, now, and as she looked at it, she suddenly remembered and all her fright came bubbling back into her neck. She was in a hole on the gap where she had said she wouldn't go, God's honour, and that meant something awful would happen. Her mother would be so angry when she got home, would nearly kill her for being so long, and Leon would be crying and crying because he wanted his milk. Ruthie felt the tears run out of her eyes as she thought of what her mother would say when she got home.

It was funny she had fallen asleep, there in her little hole with a piece of wood and bricks for a blanket. The thought of this was so funny that for a moment she forgot how frightened she was and laughed a little bit.

She thought again. I've got to go home. I'd better go home. She'll be mad, but I've got to go home. So she tried to move, but the piece of wood was so heavy, had her pinned down so firmly that she couldn't wriggle out at all. She tried to move her hands, and felt the smooth glass of the bottle of milk just as a piece of brick tumbled again, and landed against the side of her face where she could just see the sky out of one eye. So she kept still again. Bad enough to be where she was, without breaking the bottle as well. It would make her dress all wet and milky if that happened, and make her mother even angrier.

So she lay still and wondered what would happen. Would her mother come and look for her? She couldn't —not leave Leon alone in the house, and come out. And she wouldn't send anyone else to look, not here in the gap where Mrs Levy's house had been, because Ruthie had been told not to go there, and her mother wouldn't guess Ruthie had gone there—not after she had promised, God's honour, not to.

So there was nothing to do at all. Ruthie would just lie still and see what would happen. The sky she could see got bluer and darker, and for a little while she fell asleep again, dreaming about the train journey the day they had come back from Ireland, and when she woke again, it was just as though she was still in the train, because she was cold, and her legs felt all prickly and sore where she was lying on them, and she could hear people on the station talking.

Only of course it was only a dream. But she could still hear people talking. She lay very still and listened. Men's voices, shouting, calling to each other.

"Not here . . ." One of them sounded very close, almost on top of her, and a brick slithered over her face so that she couldn't see the sky any more.

"Not here, Joe. This patch went ages ago—nothing new here."

Ruthie thought for a moment. She wasn't supposed to talk to strange men, and she didn't know the voice so near to her, so perhaps she oughtn't to say anything. But then she remembered how cross her mother would be if she didn't get home soon, and perhaps this man would be a nice one, and help her get out of her hole.

So she called out, not too loudly. "Mister?"

She could hear the man's feet scrabbling on the stones, going away from her, back towards where there were other voices calling out, and she called again, louder.

"Mister! Mister!"

The scrabbling stopped, and the man's voice came suddenly very thin and high.

"Here—hold on a bit, Joe—there's someone here."

"I tell you, this patch went weeks ago—there can't be no one here. Come on, feller."

"There's someone here, I tell you. . . ."

Ruthie called out again. "Hey, mister—it's me, Ruthie!"

The stones scrabbled again, and the first voice came closer.

"There you are—didn't I tell you? Did you hear that?"

"Please, mister," Ruthie called again. "I'm stuck. Can you help me out? The wood's too heavy for me—and I might break the milk . . ."

"Hold on, ducks—hold on. Give us another shout, will yer? Come on, ducks . . ."

Ruthie thought for a minute. She didn't know just what to shout, and wondered if she should shout words or just noises.

"Come on, ducks." The stones beside her head shifted as the man above her slithered on the bricks. "Can't find yer if yer don't shout—come on, ducks."

So Ruthie shouted what they shouted at school on Empire Day. "Hip, hip hooray!" and then she stopped, because you only shouted that three times on Empire Day.

Suddenly, one of the stones over her eye, the one she hadn't been able to see through, went away, just like that, and Ruthie could look up and see the soft deep blue of the sky above. She looked at the sky and was very glad to see it again—it hadn't been nice when it had disappeared before. And then the patch went dark suddenly, and Ruthie wondered if the man had put the stone back.

"Hip, hip, hooray?' she called, not so loudly this time, and the dark patch moved, and glinted, and Ruthie could see it was a tin hat.

"Right, ducks. . . ." The man's voice was much louder now. "Got yer—hold on now—have you out in two shakes, we will. Hang about a bit, now. . . ."

And quite quickly the stones that were balanced on each other over her face were moved, so that she could see out of both her eyes really properly, and the eye that had been covered all the time could see things brighter than the other one, and Ruthie opened and shut them both in turn, enjoying the different way things looked out of each one.

The big piece of wood was moved, very slowly, and Ruthie was so glad to get rid of it, she tried to sit up, only a lot of stones came tumbling down round her, and the man said sharply, "Keep still, ducks—just leave it to us, now. Don't you go wriggling around, now . . ."

So she kept still.

And then a pair of hands got round her shoulders and she was lifted up and outwards, to be held high in the air above her hole.

"Just a kid," the man who was holding her said. "Just a kid—poor little bugger. You all right, ducks—you all right?"

"Yes, thank you," Ruthie said politely. "Thank you for getting me out—I got to go home now . . ."

"What's your name, ducks? Where do you live then?" the man said.

Ruthie looked at him, at another man standing close beside him, their tin hats glinting in the soft blueness of the evening, and at the piles of stones and bricks that were all over the place, and said, "I've got to go home now," again, because she knew you mustn't tell strange men about yourself—if they talked to you, you had

97

to run home very quickly. But the man was holding her.

She wriggled, and tried to get down from his arms.

"I got to go home," she said again, beginning to feel frightened all over again. "Please—Mummy'll be so cross—let me go home."

"I'll take yer ducks. Come on, now, where do you live?"

But Ruthie struggled harder, feeling her leg sore against the cloth of his jacket, and as she wriggled, the bottle of milk she was still clutching close against her slid from her stiff fingers and crashed against the stones below.

Ruthie stared down at the glinting glass, at the spreading pool of whiteness in the dim light, stared in sick horror at the milk that Leon was waiting for running down between the stones and bricks, and felt the tears come up again.

"Now look what you done!" she wailed. "Look what you done! My mummy'll kill me—look what you done!"

The two men looked at each other, and then the one who was holding her said wheedlingly, "Well, I tell you what—you let me take you home, and I'll tell your mum it was me what broke it, eh? And I'll give her the money for it, eh? Then she won't be mad at yer—what you say?"

Ruthie snivelled softly, and tried to think. It was bad to talk to strange men, but perhaps it was worse to break the milk, and money was always very important. If the man would tell Mummy it wasn't Ruthie who'd broken the milk and give her the money for it, perhaps it would be all right.

So she said, "I'm Ruthie Lee. I live at number nine Aspen Street, London, E.1."

"Right, ducks," the man said. "Get you there in two ticks, we will. Your mum'll be that glad to see you, you see—she won't be mad at you over the milk . . ."

"She will," Ruthie said with dreary conviction. "I said, God's honour, I wouldn't go over by Mrs Levy's and I did. She'll be mad at me . . ."

But the man only laughed, as he climbed over the stones and bricks, holding Ruthie high on his shoulder.

She turned her head as soon as she felt him start to walk on smooth ground, looking apprehensively for her mother at the window.

But she wasn't at the window. There were a knot of people round the street door, though. Black Sophie, and Mrs Fleischer and Mrs Coram, and Mrs Cohen, and Mr Levine and even old Mr Lipshitz. Ruthie stared at them all, standing there in a circle with their backs to her, and wondered what was the matter. Was her mother there, too, telling them all how naughty Ruthie was, not to have come home sooner with Leon's milk?

She began to cry again, as she could almost hear her mother shouting at her, asking her where the milk was, why she had dawdled.

"That your house over there?" the man said, and Ruthie nodded, the crying in her too thick to let her talk properly.

And then he was there, in the middle of the crowd, and the people round the street door scattered and shifted, coming round behind the man to stare over his shoulder into Ruthie's crying face.

"She's here—look, Mrs Lee—they've found her—see? She's here!"

And then she was pulled roughly from the man's arms, and it was her mother, holding her so close and tight she could hardly move or even breathe properly, and Ruthie tried to pull back, to look at her mother's face.

"I'm ever so sorry, Mummy," she began in her thick crying voice. "I'm ever so sorry, Mummy, but it wasn't me broke the milk . . ."

But her mother said nothing, just holding tightly on to her, putting her face into Ruthie's neck so that Ruthie could feel her cheek against her skin, all hot and smooth.

"Mummy?" she said again. "Are you cross, Mummy? I didn't mean it, honest—I tried to get home quick, really I did. Mummy?"

The others were all talking, chattering busily to the man who had brought her home, asking questions, talking about sending Ruthie to the country again, exclaiming over her poor mother, and Ruthie wriggled harder than ever to get back so that she could see her mother's face.

This time, she managed it, and her mother looked at her, and Ruthie looked at her mother, in the dim evening light, and Ruthie was suddenly not frightened of her any more. Her mother's face looked so different, as though some of the skin had slipped off the bones under it, all sagging, and her eyes looked very big, all puffy underneath, as though someone had stuck some putty there.

"Aren't you cross, Mummy?" she said wonderingly, suddenly knowing quite well she wasn't. "What's the matter? Why are you crying, Mummy?"

"Oh, my God," her mother said, her voice sounding different to its usual high hard sound. "Oh my God . . ." and the tears spilled over her eyes again, while Ruthie stared at her.

And then, suddenly, the sirens started again, wailing close and shrill, and the people round about scattered, started to run.

"Bring her down our shelter, Mrs Lee," Mrs Fleischer shouted. "My Lenny's here—he'll have a look at her, see she's all right. Come on, Mrs Lee—Lenny'll see to her, so go get the baby—come on, already!"

The man in the tin hat said quickly, "That's right, ducks—you go on down the shelter. I'll get the baby— where is he? Upstairs, is he? I'll get him for you—you go on down the shelter, make yourselves a nice cuppa— that's what you want—a nice cuppa . . ."

Ruthie, still held tightly, felt herself being bounced into Mrs Fleischer's house, along the passage, out into their back yard towards the shelter, and as they passed the bottom of the stairs, Lenny came down, holding a brown carrier bag, his long legs swinging as he clattered down the stairs.

"They found her, Lenny—like I said to Mrs Lee they would, they found her. She's coming so you can see she's all right—so's you can look after her!" and even in the rush along to the shelter, her voice was full of pride as she said it.

In Mrs Fleischer's shelter, Ruthie's mother sat down in the bottom bunk, holding Ruthie tightly on her lap, and Mrs Fleischer waited at the doorway for the man in the tin hat to bring Leon, and as soon as he did, shut the door firmly behind him as the crumps and rumbles began to come again, shaking the light they had hanging from the middle of the roof.

Ruthie, remembering suddenly, said, "The milk, Mummy—the man broke it, Mummy—Leon's milk."

"It's all right, shnooky, it's all right," her mother said, her voice still thick and different. "I got some from Mrs Cohen—it's all right, baby. I shouldn't have let you go— I shouldn't have let you go—it's all my fault—my God . . ." and her face went all creased and she began to cry, tears running over the putty under her eyes, streaking her face with dirt that had rubbed on to it from Ruthie's dress.

"Now, now, Mrs Lee—so it's all right, already. So don't cry—don't upset yourself with a lot of aggravation. She's here, ain't she? So all right—she's here. My Lenny —he'll make her fine, eh, Lenny? No need to cry, no need you should upset yourself no more, believe me, Mrs Lee—my Lenny, he makes sure she's all right."

Lenny sat down next to them, and smiled at Ruthie.

"So how's my best girl, eh? Got a few wallops, have you?"

"Oh, no," Ruthie said, surprised. "No one walloped me, Lenny. He was a nice man—he got me out, and he was nice—though it was him broke the milk . . ."

Lenny laughed, and looked up at his mother.

"Kids," he said, sounding very grown up, older than Mrs Fleischer even. "Kids—aren't they marvellous?"

Ruthie's mother was looking at her now, pulling at her dress to take it off, so that she could see if Ruthie was hurt, exclaiming over the bruises on her shoulders, and biting her mouth when she saw the long graze all down her leg, trying not to cry as she looked at it. But Ruthie looked down at her leg interestedly, admiring the dirty huge blood-caked mess, delighted to see a really big patch of blood.

"Will I need a bandage?" she asked and grinned a very big grin when Lenny said gravely that she would need an enormous bandage, after he had cleaned it up.

So Ruthie sat and watched him, enjoying the way her leg came clean as he mopped away with a piece of cotton wool he had taken from his carrier bag, using stuff from a bottle he also had in his bag, even enjoying the way her leg hurt as the stuff cleaned the graze.

And then, when her bandage was on, and she was tucked up in the bottom bunk with the sleeping Leon at the foot, with a big sandwich of brown bread and sardines in her hand, she thought sleepily about the way grown-ups were frightened of raids.

She knew why now, why raids were a trouble, because of the things they made happen—or the things you thought they would make happen. Really, of course, the grown-ups were a bit silly. The things you thought would happen because of the raids didn't—so it wasn't that that was frightening. It was just thinking about it that was frightening. She would have to tell them, she thought, biting at her sandwich, enjoying the way the bandage felt tight against her leg under the blanket. She would have to tell them sometime. And then she fell asleep, even before she had finished her sandwich and the voices of her mother and Mrs Fleischer and Lenny talking and the rumble of the raid outside got mixed up with the yellow light from the roof and the taste of the sardine sandwich.

CHAPTER NINE

SANDRA and Shirley and Esther were leaning on the wall behind them, and Ruthie tried to pretend she didn't know they were there. She kept her head down over her red book and tried to finish her picture of an aeroplane with bombs in it, but the picture didn't want to come any more because the girls were looking at Ruthie.

Lilian next to her on the edge of the pavement was making a picture, drawing on the ground with a piece of broken red brick, making a beautiful woman in a big dress, with a hat that covered all of her face, with a basket of flowers in her hand, and a big umbrella held in her other hand. This picture was one Lilian was very good at, and she drew it all the time. Ruthie watched her make the frilly edge on the big umbrella, and tried to pretend the big girls weren't there.

"Your leg better?" Esther said, and Ruthie kept her head down watching Lilian, as though she hadn't heard.

"Esther says, is your leg better?" Lilian said, and stopped drawing. "Esther said, Ruthie."

Ruthie stretched out her leg in its bandage and looked at it. It was better really, because it didn't feel stiff any more, but she still had a bandage on. When her mother tried to take it off she screwed up her face and said, "Fff . . ." to show it hurt but she was brave, so her mother left it on. Ruthie didn't want the bandage to come off because she liked it so much.

"Not yet," she said, and held her leg out stiff to show it wasn't better.

Esther came and squatted down on the pavement next to her, and looked at the bandage.

"What was it like when you hurt it?" She looked at Ruthie then, her eyes sliding sideways, and Ruthie, who had started to look at her, at once looked at her leg again. "Was it awful?"

Ruthie thought about what had happened in the raid, and though she didn't want to, she felt her mouth turn up in a smile. "Yes. It was awful."

The other two girls had come over now, and were sitting on the kerb too, so they were all in a row, the three big girls, and the not so big girl, and the small one who was Ruthie. Shirley leaned forwards and put her chin on her knees, so that she could look at Ruthie along the row, and she opened her eyes very wide.

"Were there rats?"

"Rats?" said Ruthie.

"My mum says there's rats where the bombs were. They eat all the dead people underneath. They start at their fingers, and then they eat their ears, and then their cheeks, so that they've got holes in their faces and their teeth show through. Great big rats."

"And if there's someone who isn't dead yet, they eat them, too, until they are," Sandra said in a very soft voice. "All the time they go nibble nibble nibble till their teeth show through the holes in their faces. Were there rats where you were, Ruthie?" and the three big girls looked at each other and giggled and shoved at each other with their shoulders.

Ruthie looked at her legs, one with its bandage and the other with the browny-blue circles showing on the skin, and thought about it. Were there rats? She couldn't remember properly. She wrinkled up her eyes till everything looked hazy and sparkly at the edges and tried to see what it had been like in the raid. After a moment of trying, she could see it. She could see her legs stretched out under the lump of wood, and her hands holding the bottle of milk, and then she couldn't see any more.

Lilian, next to her, breathed hard and put her hand out to touch the bandage on Ruthie's leg.

"Ooh, Ruthie, was there? Was there rats? It must be awful to be ate by rats. . . ."

And now Ruthie could see them, see them walking about on her legs, the big dark-coloured rats with tails like string, like the dead one Mrs Levine had found in the shelter once, only these were alive, and walking about on her legs.

She opened her eyes properly, and looked at the girls in a row next to her, at Sandra leaning forwards, at

Shirley and Esther with their shiny eyes and the smooth smiles on their faces and she said comfortably, "Oh, yes. There were rats."

Shirley's face changed a bit, not so smooth now. "Go on," she said. "I bet there wasn't."

"There was!" Ruthie could see them now, without wrinkling her eyes up, see them quite clearly, walking about on her legs under the lump of wood. "There were —oh, I think there were seven of them, all walking about on my legs, eating me."

"Ooh, Ruthie," Lilian wailed. "There wasn't!"

"Yes, there *was*!" Ruthie was annoyed. "I wouldn't say there was if there wasn't." The rats walked about on her legs more quickly, sniffing with their pointed noses. "Seven of them."

The rats all moved on to one of her legs, the one with the bandage, pushing their noses against the edge of the bandage so they could eat her leg underneath it. She wrinkled her eyes again, so that the bandage would go away from what she was seeing, but it stayed there, so the rats pushed their noses under the edge, and started to nibble.

"They ate me like anything," she said. "All the time. That's why my leg's sore." And she moved it, and said, "Fff," softly.

"You ain't 'alf a liar," Esther said, but not with any real crossness in her voice, looking at Ruthie with a smile across her wide face, all her teeth showing. "You're a rotten old liar."

"I'm not so!" Ruthie said. "You see if I am. I got a bandage on, haven't I?" and she stuck her leg out even further so they all had to look at it.

They sat quiet for a while, saying nothing, Lilian looking at Ruthie's leg with her face all worried, and Sandra and Shirley not smiling any more, but staring over the road at the gap where Mrs Levy's house had been. Esther sat and smiled, twisting her finger round and round in a piece of her hair, and Ruthie sat and watched the rats go away when the men came and got her out, all of them running under the stones. It was nice to watch it happening.

"You was there five hours," Esther said softly after a while. "Didn't you want to go to the lav all that time?"

"No," said Ruthie, dreamily, watching the men carry her back to the crowd of women in Aspen Street.

"Wouldn't it be awful if you had to go, if you couldn't hold on any more, and you got all—messy," Esther said, very softly now. "And when the men came, you were all wet. Wouldn't it be awful?"

Ruthie felt her face get stiff the way it did when people talked about being wet, and said nothing, and the picture of the men carrying her went away, and she was just looking at the sun hot on the road of Aspen Street.

"Suppose you had to go Number Two . . ." Shirley giggled, and shoved Esther with her shoulder. "Suppose it was that, and then the men came, and you were all . . ." and she giggled some more, bubbly, in her throat.

"And the men'd have to take your knickers off,

wouldn't they?" Esther said, her fingers turning rhythmically in her hair, her eyes shining again, staing at the road like Ruthie was. "They'd have to take your knickers off, because of it, and then they'd . . ." she took a deep breath—"they'd have to wipe you, wouldn't they? And then they'd smack your behind, all bare, they'd smack it and smack it, holding you over their shoulders so you couldn't move, they'd smack you, for being all dirty, and you'd have no knickers on. . . ." Her voice sounded thick, and Ruthie looked at her, though she didn't want to, but she couldn't help it.

"And they'd carry you back to your house, all bare, and they'd take you up to your bed, and throw you on it, and keep on smacking you until you fainted, and went all limp—all limp, with your eyes shut, and your head thrown back, and your hair falling over the edge of your bed. . . ."

Ruthie thought about the men who had found her, tried to see them smacking her, but they wouldn't. They just carried her, and talked and called her ducks.

"They were nice," she said.

Esther looked at her then, and stopped twisting her fingers in her hair, and then she shoved at Sandra.

"You don't know nothing, you don't. You're just a baby, you are. You don't know nothing, and you're a liar. Rats and all that! You're a rotten liar."

"I am not! And I know lots of things."

"No, you don't!"

"I do so. Lots of things. Things you don't know."

Ruthie stared at her, and made her face look angry, but she wasn't really. A bit of her was a bit surprised because the big girls were talking to her properly, as though she were their friend, were taking no notice of Lilian who was sitting all quiet. The big girls were just talking to Ruthie, showing they knew how she was getting nearer and nearer to being like them.

"What do you know?" Shirley said, shoving her face towards Ruthie. "What do you know? I bet you don't know nothing."

"I bet I do," Ruthie said. "You try and see."

"I bet you don't know about the things in the teachers' lavs at school," Sandra said suddenly. "You don't know about them, do you?"

"What things?" Ruthie blinked, trying to think. "Anyway, you can't go in there."

"We been in there, haven't we, Esther?" Shirley said, and Esther nodded very slowly.

"We've been in there. And we looked. I bet you don't know about what's in the tin at the back, do you."

"I do so," Ruthie said, but she knew they didn't believe her.

"There's things in there . . ." Shirley nodded her head. "Awful things, they are."

"I know," said Ruthie.

"What things?" Lilian sounded breathless, her voice a bit scratchy because she hadn't been talking. "Tell us, Shirley. Go on, tell us . . ."

"You're not old enough to tell." Shirley sounded

triumphant. "You're only nine. You're not old enough."

"Yes, she is," Ruthie said. "She's nearly as old as you. You're not twelve yet." It made it sound younger than saying she was eleven, saying she wasn't twelve yet.

"I'll be thirteen in a little while," Esther said. "I'll be twelve next week, and when you're twelve, you're nearly thirteen. You're in your thirteenth year. And my mum says she's going to tell me everything then, when I'm in my thirteenth year, because that's when you got to know. But I know already." And she laughed. "And I told you, didn't I, Shirl? I'm the one that knows everything first, aren't I?" and the other big girls nodded.

"What's in the teachers' lav, then?" Lilian said again, and the girls looked at each other.

And then Esther said softly, "What'll you give me if I tell you?"

"I haven't got nothing to give you." Lilian looked worried suddenly. "I haven't got nothing. Tell us, Esther, go on."

Ruthie looked at Lilian's face, and felt very big, bigger than any of them, though she was the youngest.

"I got some chocolate, Lilian."

She took the chocolate out of her gas mask case, carefully undoing the buttons, and taking out the chocolate in its blue paper and putting it down on the pavement.

"That's because you don't want to let on you don't know neither," Esther said. "'Nt it? That's why you're giving Lilian the chocolate!"

"No, it's not!" Now the chocolate was out of her gas

mask case and she could see it, Ruthie wanted it for herself after all. She had been saving it up for eating in bed, and now she was sorry she had felt big enough to be nice to Lilian who wanted to know. "No, it's not," and she put her hand out to take the chocolate back.

But Esther had taken it, and put it in her pocket.

"I'll tell you," she said softly, and they all sat very still, Lilian staring at her, Ruthie looking at her gas mask case that hadn't got chocolate in it any more and looked different because the chocolate wasn't inside it, and the other two girls smiled at Esther, saying nothing.

"There's . . .' Esther paused—"things that smell. A dirty smell."

"Like Number Two?" Lilian said breathlessly.

"Worse than that. Much worse." Esther put her head close to Lilian and said in almost a whisper, "They're STs."

"STs?" Lilian said in an ordinary voice.

"Shh!" Esther looked over her shoulder, but there was no one in near enough to hear, just the few women outside Black Sophie's in the hot afternoon sunshine. "STs. And the ones in the tin are all bloody—all covered in brown bad blood. That's what happens when it comes out. It goes all brown and it smells bad."

"Comes out of where?" Ruthie said.

Esther looked at her, very close to her, so that all Ruthie could see was eyes, and she stared into one of them, wanting to move her own eyes so that she looked at each of Esther's in turn, but she couldn't.

"When you're in your thirteenth year it starts. Blood comes out of you, out of your private, and you have to wear STs, and put them in the tins in the lavatories, and when that happens, you can have liberties taken, and get into trouble."

"What trouble?" Ruthie tried to see blood coming out of her private, but she couldn't.

"Boys. They take liberties. And you get into trouble. And if they see the STs, all bloody and everything, then your face goes yellow."

"Yellow? Why?" Lilian sounded as though she didn't believe Esther.

"Yellow like a lemon, all over your face, and your tongue and your teeth, and your eyes, all yellow. That's why they mustn't see."

"But you mightn't know they'd seen," Lilian said.

"Yes, you would. You'd wake up in the morning, and you'd be all yellow, and then you'd know a boy had seen, and then he might take liberties and you'd get into trouble."

"You're a liar," Ruthie said flatly.

But Esther just smiled, so that Ruthie knew it was true.

Lilian stood up. "I'm goin' home," she said. "My mum said I got to go home for tea early." She shuffled one foot on the ground, and stared at Esther. "I got to go."

Esther looked up at her and smiled her smooth smile again.

"If you tell your mum you know, now, your face'll go yellow."

"It can't. I—I got no—what you said. It can't go yellow. And you said it was if boys saw it."

"It happens if you tell, an 'all," Esther said.

Lilian sat down again, and looked at Ruthie.

"D'you believe her, Ruthie?"

"No."

"You do though, don't you?" Esther said. "It's true, 'nt it, Ruthie? Not like the rats. This is true."

"Tell her about the hair on you, Esther," Shirley said.

And Sandra nodded, too, and said, "Go on, Esther. You tell them."

"When you get near the blood coming, you get hair on your private," Esther said, and stared at Lilian and Ruthie.

"No, you don't," Ruthie said at once, but not because she didn't believe her. Inside her head, she knew it was true, knew it was all true. There was the cotton wool her mother burned in the fireplace or put in the dustbin wrapped in paper. That was true. And it was all the same thing Esther was saying.

"I'll show you, if you like. If you give me some more chocolate I'll show you."

"I haven't got any more."

"Next time you get some, you can give me that. And I'll show you."

Shirley stood up, and shoved at Sandra with her foot,

so that Sandra stood up, too, and then the two of them went along the pavement to the alleyway by Mrs Cohen's.

Esther sat still for a second, and then she got up too, and went after them, looking back over her shoulder at the younger girls.

"Come on, then, and I'll show you."

Lilian and Ruthie sat still for a little while, and then, not looking at each other, they got up and went to the alleyway as well.

Esther was standing against the wall in the coolness of the shadows, with Sandra and Shirley standing each side of her, and the three of them looked at the two smaller ones, the same smile on their faces.

Very slowly, Esther pulled her dress up and held the hem under her chin, watching the girls' faces under her eyebrows all the while.

Ruthie stood very still, staring, watching the hands with the black edges round their nails, watching them very slowly pull Esther's knickers down, so that her skin showed, so that her belly button showed, and then, the knickers were right down, just the middle part held between Esther's fat legs.

It was very quiet in the alleyway, only the soft noise of traffic from Festival Street coming in, and the sound of Lilian breathing thickly next to her.

And Ruthie looked, and saw the soft straight lines of black, all the little lines pointing downwards, making a triangle that ended with its point against Esther's white knickers.

"You can touch it if you like," Esther said.

Ruthie didn't move. She just looked at the black lines, at the knickers between Esther's fat legs.

"Go on. Touch it," Esther said.

Sandra leaned forwards, and put one finger against the hair, and giggled, and then Shirley did, but Lilian and Ruthie just stood very still.

"Scaredy cat," said Esther, and suddenly pulled her knickers up again, and pulled her dress down, wriggling her bottom against the wall as she straightened it.

"If you forget the chocolate, your face'll go yellow. Because I'll tell your mum you know. All yellow, and then everyone'll know you found out, and the boys'll think you got STs, and take liberties, and you'll get into trouble. The next twice you get chocolate, you give it to me, Ruthie. And you, Lilian. You get more'n I do."

Lilian turned and ran, away down the alleyway, back to Festival Street.

Esther laughed, and said again. "The next twice, Ruthie, or I'll tell."

Shirley and Sandra giggled, and then the three of them went, arms round each other's shoulders, out of the Festival Street end of the alleyway, and Ruthie was standing alone, looking at the bricks on the wall and thinking of nothing at all, just counting the bricks with her eyes.

After a minute or two she bent down and took the bandage off her leg, unwinding it so that it showed a line between the clean underneath part and the dirty top part. And she dropped it on the ground, and walked home, not limping any more the way she had ever since the night of the raid. It didn't matter any more now.

CHAPTER TEN

———

SHE was making a picture like Lilian's, the one of the lady in the big dress, kneeling on the hot pavement and drawing with big soft lines. The lines came big because the chalk was hot and soft from being in the sun. It was when she looked up for a moment, to stare up the street while she tried to remember what came next in the picture, that she saw him.

He was walking towards her, rolling a bit from side to side the way he always did—swaggering, her mother used to call the way he walked. He was wearing brown, like the men at the station, with a long narrow hat on his head, his curly hair standing up a bit on each side of it.

She wasn't really surprised to see him: it was as though she'd known he would be there when she looked up, known she would see him swaggering along like he always had. Because she had really known she would see him, she didn't do anything, just bent over again, and did another line on the picture, because she suddenly remembered the umbrella came next.

He came and stopped next to her so that his shadow went all over her picture.

"Hello, Ruthie," he said, very softly.

"Hello, Daddy," Ruthie said, and looked up at him. The sun was shining so brightly round his head it looked as though he had a gold plate over it, like the pictures on the wall at school of men in long white dresses with gold plates on their heads.

"You're getting big," he said after a minute, staring at her.

"Yes," Ruthie said.

"Where is she?"

"Upstairs. Do you want her?"

"Yes."

"The door's open," Ruthie said, and started to draw again.

He leaned over and pulled on her arm so that she had to stand up.

"Go up and tell her, eh, Ruthie? Give her a surprise?"

"All right," Ruthie said, and wiped her chalky hands on her dress before she turned to go into the house.

"Here—just a minute." He took his hat off, and it went flat in his hand, and the button on it shone golden in the sun.

"Give her this, eh? Don't say anything—just give it her."

"All right." Ruthie said again, and took the hat and went in. It was cool in the house, and she ran her hands along the cool banisters as she went up the stairs, counting them as she always did.

"Eleven, twelve, thirteen—Mummy? Where are you?"

She was in the kitchen, sitting at the table, and Leon was on the floor, crawling about.

Ruthie went over to the table and put the hat down in front of her mother, on top of the paper she was reading.

Her mother looked at it, and then put out her hand as though she were going to touch the hat, but she didn't. She just stared at it.

"Where'd you get this?" and her voice sounded very thick, like it had the night of the raid when Ruthie's leg got hurt.

"He said to give it to you."

"Who said?"

"Daddy," Ruthie said, and stared at the hat too. She'd known she would see him, really, but it was funny to be standing there looking at the hat when he was down in the street. "He said to give it to you for a surprise."

"Oh, my God!" her mother said. "Oh, my God!"

"Shall I give it back to him?" Ruthie asked, but her mother said nothing, just looked at the hat on the newspaper.

Then Ruthie heard him, heard the stairs creak a bit as he walked on them. There was a quiet moment when he got to the top, and then he walked again, and there he was, standing in the doorway.

"Bessie?"

"He's come up, Mummy," Ruthie said, looking at her mother, but she just sat very still staring at the hat.

"Bessie? Are you going to throw it back at me?" and then he gave a thick sort of laugh. "You said always to throw my hat in first. Are you going to throw it back?"

"Go downstairs, Ruthie." Her mother's voice wasn't thick any more, just high and bright the way it was when there were people about. "Go down and play. Don't come up till I call you. And, Ruthie—take Leon. You can sit on the step with him. Don't let him crawl on the road, just sit on the step with him."

"All right," said Ruthie, and picked up Leon, and went to the door. Her father came in so she could get through the door, and when she got to the top of the stairs, Leon heavy in her arms, he shut the door, click, so that she was alone with Leon in the dimness.

She sat on the step with Leon for a long time, holding him on her lap, and after a while Leon fell asleep, his head against her bare arm, and she liked that, rocking a bit from side to side, and pretending he was her baby and she was the mother, and he slept, and his hair got damp because he was sweating, and she could feel the dampness on her skin.

She could hear their voices upstairs, coming sometimes loud, sometimes softly, from the window, her mother's high and thin, her father's heavy and rumbling a bit. And then the voices stopped, and still Ruthie sat on the step with Leon.

Mrs Fleischer came out of her house after a while, and when she saw Leon asleep on Ruthie's lap came tiptoeing over to her, like someone pretending to be very quiet, though she made quite a lot of noise really, a creaking noise when she moved. That was because of her corsets. Ruthie knew that because once she'd asked Mrs Fleischer, and Mrs Fleischer had laughed and told Ruthie what the creaking was.

"So who's a little momma, then, eh, Ruthie?" Mrs Fleischer whispered very loudly, and Leon moved his head in his sleep, but he didn't wake up.

"I am," Ruthie said. "I'm a mother."

"So what you doin' down here with him, Ruthie? Shouldn't you take him up so he could sleep in his cot, eh?"

"They're busy. Mummy said to stay here."

"So who's busy?"

"Mummy and Daddy." Ruthie looked down at Leon and moved her arm a little because it was getting stiff, but Leon still stayed asleep.

Mrs Fleischer stopped whispering. "Who?"

"Mummy and Daddy."

"Your *daddy*'s up there?"

"Yes. I took his hat up and then he went up. He's a soldier nebbish," Ruthie said, and then smiled at Mrs Fleischer. "Did you know that? He's a soldier nebbish."

"He's in *uniform*? In khaki?"

Ruthie nodded. "A soldier nebbish," she said again, patiently.

She was used to telling people things lots of times because they didn't listen properly. "I took his hat up first and then he came up, and Mummy said to . . ."

But Mrs Fleischer didn't wait to listen any more. She was hurrying down the street towards Black Sophie's shop, her back moving solidly over her thick legs which were nearly running, she was in such a hurry.

She went into the shop, and after a minute, they came out, all the women who were there, Black Sophie, and Mrs Fleischer and the others, and they stood and talked with their heads near each other, all staring up at Ruthie's house.

The sound came then, from a long way at first, then closer. The women shifted and moved apart, like the ducks in the park when someone threw bread on the lake for them, began to move up the street towards Ruthie, and the siren got louder, and Ruthie stood up so quickly that Leon woke up and began to cry, just like the siren.

Mrs Fleischer got to her own door and shouted at Ruthie. "Come in mine, Ruthie! Bring the baby, boobalah —come in my shelter."

But Ruthie shook her head, and went into the house. She'd have liked to go into Mrs Fleischer's shelter but she'd have to ask Mummy first, or there'd be a row.

Leon was still crying, pulling away from Ruthie, and then her mother came down the stairs. She wasn't wearing her dress any more. She had her thick dressing gown on, and her hair was untidy like it was when she first got up in the morning.

"Give him here." She took Leon and pushed Ruthie towards the back door and the shelter.

"Where's Daddy? Isn't he coming down?"

"Hurry up—hurry *up*! The guns are starting. . . ."

Ruthie could hear them, rolling and grumbling far away, and then there was a thicker noise, and the floor shook a little and her mother pushed her harder, out into the yard.

"Hurry *up*—for God's sake, move!"

He came then, hurrying out of the house across the yard, his brown shirt unbuttoned, hanging out over his trousers, and Ruthie looked at his feet, saw he had nothing on them, not even socks, and she laughed. But she couldn't hear her laughing because there was more rumbling from the guns, and more of the banging that made the ground shake. The shaking was like the wobbling you could see in the air over the hot road when you sat on the pavement and looked at the hotness. Her father was looking up into the sky, holding his hand over his eyes because of the brightness of the sun.

"Look—see over there—see, Bessie? Three of the buggers—see them? Over there . . ."

"Come *on*!" and then they were all in the shelter, in the damp smell of it, and her mother was lighting the oil lamp, and the door was shut tight against the sun and the heat and the noise.

She woke up when her mother began to take her clothes off. She was stiff because she had been lying on one leg

125

in her sleep, but when she moved her leg the prickling feeling didn't matter because she could feel she was quite dry—not even a little damp the way she was if she'd had an accident a long time ago and it had started to get dry.

"I'm hungry," she said, blinking a little against the suddenly bright oil lamp. "I'm hungry, Mummy."

"So you'll have to stay hungry. There's only biscuits here, and we're staying all night. You can sleep in your vest and knickers—come on, now," and her mother wrapped her in the rough blanket and pushed her down on the bunk again.

"Where's Mr Levine? Where's Mrs Levine?" Ruthie said, then, because looking round she could only see her father sitting in the corner, a cigarette in the corner of his mouth, his eyes squinting while he looked at the book he was holding sideways to the light, the smoke from his cigarette curling up into his eyes.

"I don't know. They never came home. They're in a shelter somewhere else. Go to sleep—here, just a minute. You'd better use the bucket first. Come on."

So Ruthie got out of the bunk and used the bucket and then got back onto the bunk, careful not to touch Leon, asleep at the other end of it.

"Can't I have a biscuit? I'm hungry."

"Oh, all right—only, for God's sake, go to sleep."

The biscuit was a big one, all crumbly and sweet, and Ruthie nibbled all round it very slowly to make it last a long time. She could hear the noise still, loud rumbling and crunching noises, and the lamp kept

shaking, every time there was a crunch. And she fell
asleep again.

And she was dry in the morning, too, when she woke
to see her father standing by the open door of the
shelter, looking out into the brightness of the early
day.

"I'm dry. I'm dry," she whispered to herself as she
put her dress and sandals on. "I'm dry."

They had breakfast; bread and cream cheese and tea,
and an apple each for Ruthie and Leon. All the time at
breakfast, they were quiet, her father just sitting and
eating very quickly and drinking three big cups of tea,
her mother having only tea, but no one said anything.
Her mother's face was long and tight this morning, with
the lines by her nose and mouth showing very clearly,
and Ruthie knew if she talked her mother would shout
at her, so she just ate her breakfast and said nothing.

When he'd finished eating her father looked at her.

"You'd better go to school, Ruthie."

"It's the holidays," Ruthie said, surprised. "We
started last week. It's the holidays."

He looked at her, and then he began to laugh, very
loudly, his face getting redder and redder.

"Christ, it's the holidays—the holidays," and some
spit came out of his mouth he laughed so much.

"Go wash yourself, Ruthie," her mother said then.
"Go on. You'd better clean up, too," but she didn't
look at Ruthie's father when she said that, only bent over

Leon to wipe his sticky face after he'd finished drinking from his cup.

Ruthie washed, enjoying the smell of the soap, the green soap that smelled so good you could almost eat it. She'd tried it once to see if it tasted as nice as it smelled, but it didn't, and the taste had stayed in her mouth for a long time, sickly and horrible.

"I need some sleep," her father said suddenly into the quietness of the room.

"Sure you do. You got work to do, eh?" Ruthie's mother said.

"So there's no need to bitch, is there? Work or not, I need sleep. I haven't slept in a bed this past week, you hear me? Not this past week. . . ."

"You're breaking my heart."

"Ah, Bessie—Bessela—don't go on like this. So could I help it? Could I? They picked on me, I tell you— picked on me. I couldn't stand it—and if I'd stayed they'd have had me God knows where by now, dead, maybe. That what you want? I should be killed in this stinking war? That's what you want, eh?"

"And is it my fault?" Ruthie watched her mother, watched her face go round again as her voice got higher and higher and louder. "I started the war? It's my fault you joined the army? I got to live on the Guardians, on lousy handouts from those bloody Rabbis because you can't be a man, you can't stay where you can get money for your wife and children to eat on? So I got to be pleased to see you, I got to be happy when you come running back like the stinking animal that you are?"

"You were glad enough to see me yesterday," his voice was soft then. "You didn't say no to . . ."

Ruthie screamed then, because her mother suddenly flew across the room, was scratching at her father's face, her face twisted and ugly, and then Leon screamed, too, and her mother turned away from her father, and shouted at Ruthie, "Go downstairs! Go out into the street—go on and wait there!"

And Ruthie ran out and downstairs, her legs shaking and wobbling under her, her throat feeling thick and tight so that she couldn't swallow. She could see it still inside her eyes, her mother's hands curved widely against her father's face, his head pulled back and his mouth open as he grabbed at the curved fingers and pulled them away from his face.

She sat on the step, just inside the door, where people couldn't see her, and she cried, the tears hot on her face, and the shaking inside her going on and on as though it would never stop.

It was like it was at school, when boys in the playground started to fight. She remembered it then, how Lilian once had made her climb on the wall and hold on to the hard bricks with her fingers to watch the boys in their playground hitting each other, and rolling about on the ground. It had been just like now, the thick feeling in her throat, the shaking in her legs, and she had cried because it was so awful to see people hit each other.

She didn't hear her mother come down the stairs

because she was crying so much, not until she felt herself picked up did she know she was there.

"It's all right, baby, it's all right. Don't cry, sweetheart, don't—please don't . . ."

And when Ruthie saw her mother was crying, too, it was worse than ever, and they stayed there in the dim hallway, Ruthie holding tightly to her mother, feeling her arms warm and strong round her, and they cried together. And then it was better. The feeling in her throat went away, and the shaking feeling went away, too, and Ruthie's mother put her down on the floor, and wiped her face on her handkerchief, and smoothed her hair with her hands, and then wiped her own face, and smiled at Ruthie, a small thin smile.

"We're going out, baby. Just wait a minute while I get Leon, and we'll go out."

"Where is *he*?"

Ruthie's mother looked thin-faced again.

"Asleep. It's only us who are going out—you and me and Leon. He's asleep."

When they came out into the street, some of the women were standing by Mrs Fleischer's door, talking, their heads close and nodding.

"Bessie! You've heard?"

Ruthie's mother stopped, standing leaning forward a little to show she was in a hurry, wanted to walk down the street.

"I can't stop now . . ."

"The Levines—you haven't heard?"

"What's to hear?" and now Ruthie's mother stood straight, and shifted Leon to her other arm. "What's happened?"

"They were in the Chiltern Street shelter—down by the workshop, in the public shelter—and they got it direct. My Lenny was on at the hospital when they brought the people there—thirty-seven killed, he says, no one left of all of them, and the Levines, they was there."

Mrs Fleischer began to cry, but her eyes were bright under the crying, and she talked without any of the noises people make when their crying is coming from right inside them.

"Oh, my God," Ruthie's mother said. "I can't—oh, my God."

"You'll stay here?" Mrs Fleischer wasn't crying any more, and looked closely at Ruthie's mother. "You can pay the whole rent for the house? And their things— what'll you do about them?"

Black Sophie came out of the little crowd of women then. "He's back, Bessie? Come back? Is he goin' to tell them he's here, eh? Go back to the army? You said when he comes back you'll go away with the children— eh?"

Ruthie's mother shook her head, and said nothing. She just pushed through the crowd, holding onto Ruthie's hand and with Leon over her shoulder, and the three of them went hurrying down Aspen Street towards Commercial Road.

CHAPTER ELEVEN

DOWN Aspen Street, across Commercial Road, through the traffic, past the shops and the people, and Ruthie's mother walked so fast that Ruthie had to run to keep up. Every so often, her mother shifted Leon to her other arm, and her face was damp with sweat as she went along. Ruthie looked up at her, and thought of something suddenly.

"Where's the pram, Mummy? I'd forgotten. Where is it? I haven't seen it. Why isn't Leon in the pram?"

"The pram? You've eaten it," Ruthie's mother said, and then laughed in a loud voice. "You've eaten it. And if they ask me why I did it, I'll tell them, I'll tell him, because the kids had to eat the pram and I had to kill myself humping a heavy baby with no pram."

"I didn't! Honestly, I didn't," Ruthie said loudly. The things she had really done were bad enough. She didn't want to be blamed for something she hadn't done. "I couldn't eat a *pram*."

"I sold it. Now, shut up . . ." Her mother stopped then,

leaned against a wall for a moment, Leon up against her shoulder.

"Oh, God. I'm sorry, Ruthie. It isn't your fault. I shouldn't talk to you like that. Bad enough the way it is for you, I shouldn't talk to you like that—I'm sorry, Ruthie, boobalah."

Ruthie looked up at her, and said the way Mrs Ward at school said when you explained something to her, "That's all right. I understand."

Her mother looked at her, in a close sort of way, as though she were looking at her properly for the first time.

"Do you, Ruthie? Do you? Maybe you do, at that. Maybe I don't think about you enough the way I should—though, God knows, I think and think what should I do for you—do you understand, Ruthie?"

It was funny standing there in the busy road, against the wall by the baker's shop, listening to her mother talking to her in the sort of voice she used when she talked to the women in Black Sophie's shop. She knows, Ruthie thought. She knows I'm getting as big as the other girls, and that's what she means.

"I think I do," she said, trying to talk like a big person would, like the women did in Black Sophie's shop. "I try to, but I can't always. . . ."

Her mother stared at her for a long time, then she moved, and began to walk again.

"I'll tell you. I'll call them, then I'll tell you. You got a right to know why. I'm doing it for you, after all, aren't I? You and Leon. And he can't understand, Christ knows, he can't. But when he can, if I'm not here to tell him, I want he should know, and you'll tell him, eh, Ruthie? You'll tell him why. I'll call them first—then I'll tell you."

Round the corner into Watney Street, past the public house on the corner where decent people didn't go, God should forbid, past the stalls in the market, past the library to the park. Across the park and the yellow worn grass, past the benches to the other side, where the three red telephone boxes were, with brown paper criss-crossed on their little square windows.

They stopped then. Ruthie's mother pushed Ruthie down onto the bench, and put Leon on her lap.

"Sit here. I got to make a call. Then—just sit here."

Ruthie watched her mother in the telephone box, watched her through the criss-crossed paper on the glass, over the sandbags piled round the bottom of the box, and tried to work out what the words were her mother was saying into the telephone she held so close to her face. But she couldn't. She could see her mouth move, her eyebrows moving when her mouth did, but all Ruthie could hear was traffic, and Leon bubbling and snuffling on her lap.

Her mother put the phone down then, and stood still inside the box staring at the mirror over the phone. After a while she leaned forwards and pulled at her hair, staring in the mirror, but not as though she could really see herself doing it, just doing it because the mirror was there and that was what you did when there was a mirror.

She came out of the box then, and sat down next to Ruthie on the bench.

Ruthie looked at her, and said, "He's ever so heavy. Can I put him down on the grass in the park?"

"Mmm? Oh. Yes. All right. We'll go in the park."

They sat on the grass, all three of them, and Leon crawled a little bit, but came back every time. Ruthie just sat, and looked down at the grass, watching the little ants running in between the grass stems, and she wondered how it looked to be so little, to run about next to grass that looked as big as trees because you were so little. Did ants have shelters? She began to watch ants going into very small shelters under the ground.

"It's a terrible thing, isn't it, Ruthie? To do such things when you don't want to but you got to?"

Ruthie looked at her mother, and forgot to think about the ants in their shelters under the ground. Her mother had that grown-up voice again, and Ruthie straightened her shoulders so she should look like a grown-up.

"I do terrible things I don't want to sometimes," she said.

"Do you, Ruthie? Like what?"

Ruthie looked at her, and then away, staring across the park to the low wall where the railings used to be, but where there were now only stumps, because the railings had been taken for salvage.

"Like getting wet. I don't want to, but it just happens."
Ruthie felt her chest begin to shake. Talking about being
wet made her chest shake a lot inside.

"This is different," her mother said, as though she
hadn't really noticed Ruthie was talking about being a
pisher. "This I could help, I suppose—if I wanted to
go on like I am. But how could I help it, Ruthie? The
pram I've sold—what else've I got to sell? And with the
Levines gone, what else can I do? I can't pay no rent
for the whole house—and I can't sell their things, can
I? Somewhere they got family—someone'll come to
get their things, you see if they don't—and if I go and sell,
then where am I? In dead trouble, that's where. And if
they put me in prison what happens to you and Leon?"

"Mummy!" Ruthie stopped trying to look grown up
and moved so that she was kneeling next to her mother.
"What do you mean? You're not going to . . ."

"No, no, baby, it's all right. But like I said, what else
could I do? All I got left of my own I could sell is my
wedding ring, and that's worth a fat lot." She stretched
her hand out and looked at the narrow yellow ring on
her finger. "A fat lot I'd get for that, believe me. So I
had to do it, you see, Ruthie? I had to, whether I wanted
or not."

"Had to do what, Mummy?"

Ruthie's mother didn't seem to hear. "If I let him go
on the way he is, what happens to us? I got to get some
money coming in somehow. This way, they'll pay my
allowance again, you see? The woman at the Council,

she told me. When they get him, they pay the allowance again. Three months it's been, Ruthie. Three months, and nothing coming in but what the Guardians gave me, and the way they are, that'll stop soon, the way they hang on to their lousy money."

Ruthie didn't understand, but she said again, "I understand, Mummy," because her mother had been pleased when she'd said it before.

"You won't hate me for it, Ruthie?" her mother said, and put her arm round Ruthie and held her close.

"I couldn't hate you, Mummy—not even when you get mad at me," Ruthie said, feeling pleased with herself. She was saying all the right sort of things, she knew that. She felt her mouth make a smooth round smile because she was so pleased with herself. It didn't matter it was a lie, because sometimes she hated her mother very much, quite often really. But that didn't matter.

"Oh, Ruthie, baby, you're the best friend I've got, boobalah, my big daughter—the best friend I've got . . ." and then she was sniffing and crying, holding Ruthie close.

Ruthie wriggled so that she could stroke her mother's hand. "It's all right, Mummy. I'll never hate you," and she listened to her voice saying it, and watched herself stroking her mother's hand like a grown-up person would, and laughed a bit inside. Her mother looked so silly, sitting on the grass and sniffing like Leon did.

"I did it for you, you know? You and Leon. If they ask you, and they will, those lousy women, they'll find out and they'll ask you, you'll tell them, eh, Ruthie? Why did she shop him, Ruthie? That's what they'll say, and then you'll tell them, eh, lovey?"

"Mummy did it for me and Leon," Ruthie said and stroked her mother's hand some more.

Her mother stopped crying after a while, and then Ruthie said, "What's shop him, Mummy?"

Her mother looked at her, and smiled a thin sort of smile.

"What I just did. Your father ran away from the army, lovey, see? And so I got no money from them while he was on the run. And now he's come back and I've shopped him—I told the army he's here, and they'll come and get him, and I'll get my money again. Maybe I buy you a new dress, eh, Ruthie?"

"Yes," said Ruthie. "A yellow one, with ships on, like Lilian's got. I'd like a dress like that."

Ruthie's mother laughed then, and got up, and picked up Leon.

"You'd rather have a dress than a father, eh, Ruthie?"

"But I've got a father," Ruthie said. "I haven't got a dress with ships on."

"Yes, you've got a father. Such a father. Come on, Ruthie. They should have gone by now. Come on."

They went back the way they had come, not hurrying now. As they got nearer to Aspen Street, Ruthie's mother walked slower and slower, until she was just dawdling the way Ruthie did sometimes.

When they got to the place opposite Aspen Street,

Ruthie's mother stopped, and stared across the road at the opening of the street, at Black Sophie's shop on the corner, at the traffic grinding along the hot road, and the people walking past.

"There's another thing, too," she said, and it was as though she were Mrs Ward at school, giving a lesson to the class, explaining to them about the lesson. "With him on the run, how could I go to the country with my children, where they'll be safe? Tens of thousands have been killed in London this summer, tens of thousands. We've escaped by a miracle, a miracle, because by rights we should be in the country. But with him running, how could I go? For all he's done to his children, his lovely children, how could I leave him not knowing where I am? That's why. I did it for his good, as well as for my children, you understand? For the good of everybody."

At the opening of Aspen Street, a car appeared, a big brown one with shapes painted on its sides in blue and green, all swirly in the bright sunshine. Ruthie looked at it carefully. It wasn't often cars came into Aspen Street, but she remembered then. This car had come before, with the soldiers in red hats and shining white gaiters on their legs. She could see them, inside the car at the front, and then the car turned out of Aspen Street, and moved into the traffic, passed a bus, and disappeared into the heat shimmer far down Commercial Road.

Ruthie looked up at her mother, and opened her mouth to say something, but then she stopped.

Her mother was crying again, staring after the car

with tears running down her face, with Leon on her shoulder and pulling at her hair though she took no notice of him doing it.

"Oh, God, Benny, you stupid bastard," she said softly, and turned her head to wipe her eyes and nose against Leon's back. And she said it in a soft warm voice, the sort of voice that Ruthie liked, that made her feel comfortable.

"Are we going home, Mummy?" Ruthie asked, and pulled on her mother's arm. "Are we going home? And can we get the dress today, the yellow one with ships on, like Lilian's?"

Her mother looked down at her, and then said, "Home? Such a home . . ."

"Are we going there?"

"You want to?"

Ruthie frowned a little, staring at her mother, trying to see in her face what answer she wanted, what she ought to say.

"I don't know."

"I never want to see the bloody place again. They can bomb it tomorrow, for all I care—tomorrow—this afternoon, you hear me? Right this afternoon, for all I care."

And then Ruthie remembered.

"Are we going back to the country? Are you sending me back to the country?"

Ruthie's mother turned, and began to walk, away from Aspen Street, along the wide pavements of Commercial Road, towards the place where the car had disappeared.

"I'll never let you go on your own again, Ruthie—I promise, never on your own again. You don't want to go on your own to the country, do you, Ruthie?"

She didn't have to think of the right answer this time. The right one was the same as she wanted to say.

"No. Not on my own. Not ever."

"All of us, you and me and Leon, eh, boobalah? Just us. We'll go to the country, and maybe they'll find us a little place of our own, eh? You'd like that. We'll have a little place of our own, with a real garden and we'll grow things, and play in the sun in the country, and you'll go to school and get a proper education again. You ought to get a proper education, because you're a clever girl, and you need a chance."

She stopped again, and held Ruthie's hand very tightly, and stared down at her. "For you, it'll be different. For you, everything good, eh, Ruthie? The war'll finish, one day it'll finish, and we'll stay safe in the country till then, and one day for you it'll be different. You'll marry a marvellous husband and you'll have a house and a car, all your own . . ."

"I'd like a car," Ruthie said.

"And an education, remember that. An education. You could be—anything, anything at all. A doctor, maybe . . ."

"Like Lenny? Can girls be doctors?"

"Sure they can. You can. You'll see. That's why I did it, see? To get you an education in the country, keep you safe, you and Leon."

They walked on. After a while Ruthie stopped thinking about having a car and driving it, and said, "Are we going to the country now?"

"We're going to the Council . . ."

"They'll send us to the country?"

"Yes. Listen, Ruthie. I want to tell you—sometimes, like I said, you do things because you got to. Even if you don't want, you got to. So listen to me . . ."

"Yes. I understand," Ruthie said again.

"We've been bombed out, you see? Bombed out last night in the raid. We tell them we lived in Chiltern Street where they got it, by the workshops there, and we got bombed out last night. We got nothing but what we stand up in, you see, Ruthie? So we got to be given some things to wear, some clothes for you and Leon, and for me, and we got to have some money, and we go to the country. They got to look after us. But you remember. We lived in Chiltern Street, we got bombed out last night, and we been with friends this morning, and now we want to be sent to the country. Don't go answering questions, you hear me? Anyone asks you, you just say you don't know, you don't remember."

"There's my books that I swopped. And my crayons," Ruthie said. "I made some pictures and I want them."

"They'll give you more, believe me they'll give you more. I'll tell them you lost all your bits of toys, God help you, and they'll give you more. Only don't go answering questions, you hear? We're going to the country, right now, we're going. I don't go back to

Aspen Street. Those lousy women they'll drive me mad if I go back—easy for them, with their husbands that don't go on the run, they'll have it in for me because I shopped him. I don't go back."

And they walked on, down Commercial Road, towards the rest centre at the Council, away from Aspen Street and the women and Black Sophie's shop, and the girls with their shiny eyes and bubbly giggles, and Festival Street and the school and the stalls in the market.

And as they walked away, the places and people disappeared. Ruthie knew that, knew they had gone, because she was never going back there to make them real again. Already she was forgetting, the way she always did. She crinkled up her eyes to see it, but it was hazy, Aspen Street was hazy and the people were hazy, without any faces because Ruthie was going away from them and they'd never be real again. But she could see Ruthie, there in the middle of Aspen Street, sitting on the kerb so that her knickers could get dry, a smaller than real Ruthie, with her gas mask round her neck and her little red book on her lap, drawing pictures of balloons. That Ruthie would always be there, the Ruthie who had come there at the beginning of the summer, that Ruthie would stay there for ever, in the place that was disappearing for ever.

The real Ruthie walked on, feeling her legs moving against her dress, feeling the heat coming up under her shoes, and she felt sad about the other Ruthie, left for ever in Aspen Street that wasn't real any more. That

Ruthie would never have an education or a car or be a doctor. Poor Ruthie, thought Ruthie. Poor Ruthie. She never even got a piece of glass for herself, a piece of lovely spiky glass with bright colours shining out of it in the sunshine. The poor thing had wanted it so much, Ruthie thought, she's sitting there on the kerbstone wanting a piece of glass and she can never have it.

Above them, the barrage balloons turned softly and gently on their cables, the rainbows round their tails bright in the blue sky. But Ruthie didn't look up at them. There wasn't any reason to look. Soon they, too, like Aspen Street, like all of London, like the sirens and the raids and the guns and the noise, the smell of hot tar from the roads, the smell of herrings and cucumbers and onions from Mrs Cohen's shop, all of it was going to disappear, because Ruthie was going away.

When we get there, to the country, I'll make a map of it, the new country place, then that will be the real place, Ruthie thought. That will be nice for the country, when I make it a real place.

As they walked, she whispered to herself, "I was Ruthie Lee. I had black hair and brown eyes and I was Ruthie Lee. I was a little girl, and I was Ruthie Lee. And now I am Ruth Lee, a big girl, a friend to my mother and it will be different for me."

And the picture of the little Ruthie Lee, sitting on the kerb in Aspen Street, disappeared from inside her head altogether, for ever and always, as Ruth Lee went to the country.